PROJECT

MW00625981

TEAM

DATE

EMERGENT
FUTURES
LAB

Emergent Futures Lab Press
emergentfutureslab.com

INNOVATING EMERGENT FUTURES
First Edition:
Summer 2021 Prototype Edition
Designed by Marco de Mel Pedersen

Iain Kerr and Jason Frasca

NOTE: You have in your possession a working draft printed
for research and development purposes. It is not intended
for general distribution. It is incomplete, contains errors and
missing citations. We really appreciate your use and welcome
any and all feedback. Thank you!

THE INNOVATION DESIGN WORKBOOK

STUDENT EDITION

PART ONE: INTRODUCING THE INNOVATION DESIGN APPROACH

iain kerr and jason frasca

"There is no work of invention that does not call on
a people who does not yet exist"
gilles deleuze

begin anywhere, no ideas but in making

Innovation, invention, and all forms of creativity are *journeys*. More than that they are strange journeys where the path — never mind the destination — *does not exist prior to you starting out on the journey.*

Then when an invention begins to take form, that too is only a beginning — *invention never ceases* — it is fundamentally excessive in every way. Creativity and invention are strange exemplary unprecedented and generative events that ultimately *make us*.

Innovation is about experimentally engaging with this excessive change (novelty, difference, the new, etc. — whatever you wish to call it), and understanding that it, like all change, is a unique aesthetic, ethical and political event with unknowable consequences...

WHO ARE YOU?

- *Are you a community group striving to design for good?*

- *Are you an entrepreneurial team with an idea you wish to develop?*

- *Are you an artist collective wishing to deepen your practice?*

- *Are you a farmer wishing to change farming?*

- *Do you already have an invention and wish to see what its capacities really are?*

- *Are you a business wondering how to innovate a radically new approach?*

- *Are you a design professional frustrated by the limits of your current practice?*

- *Are you a regional government faced with a seemingly intractable problem?*

This book comes out of our engagement with these issues and many other related questions.

And so we say: This is a book for those who have a curiosity for seeking, doing and being part of evolving transformative differences.

It is a book that only makes sense and comes alive if you use it with others as a tool for real change.

In this spirit of action, we ask you, before reading any further, to do two things:

1. Write on the inner cover what project you wish to use this book towards:

Write something about what you want to do, even — especially if you are uncertain. This might seem premature, we get it, creativity is always premature — but it really helps to have a heading. Headings set us out on a journey and free us to act without needing to know exactly what we are trying to do, and exactly where we should end up.

2. Take this book for a walk.

Why? We believe that creativity begins in action — in doing.

So let's start.

But, let's start slow.

We believe that real innovation is slow innovation.

Don't rush: start reading by putting on your walking shoes, grab a coat, tuck this book and a pencil in your pocket. Turn off your phone, and head outside. Wander with an open mind. Meander. Drift. Walk awhile thinking about your project. Follow where it might lead you: let it surprise you — let it's world surprise you.

Explore it. Come back to this book hours later in a park or a bar. Meet up with the others who are on this journey with you. Share a picnic, a drink, an evening and begin reading and doing together.

The words and actions of this book will have been awakened on your long meander through your area of interest: they are now ready for your active engagement.

Two final thoughts before we really begin:

First, over the years we have noticed in ourselves a habit that when we first think about innovating our minds immediately jump to thinking about all sorts of cool solutions, end products and big ideas.

We have found that this habit is *not* helpful.

Obsessing about solutions at the beginning of the innovation process *makes invention impossible* and kills the very possibility of creation.

We all have countless answers and solutions in our heads. And the creative process is often triggered by the thought of a solution.

But remember the new is really new — it does not exist until it is made — it cannot be something we already know and can describe. So our great solution — no matter how cool it is — it's not new.

As you begin the innovation process don't hold onto that imagined perfect solution or chase after making that one perfect final invention or answer to anything, — *slow down, let go of reflexive habits, embrace the strange journey of invention, let it transform you and know that the new will emerge when you least expect it.*

And the second thought: There are many forms and goals of innovation. This book does not cover all of these, it is designed with the express purpose of assisting in the process of producing innovations that open up new worlds, new ways of doing things and new ways of being alive. Thus, while other books and processes might focus on other forms of developmental creativity and invention, our primary focus is on qualitative change and worldmaking - *How to Innovate*.

welcome
what
comes
next

CONTENTS

Part 1: Introducing Creativity

Part 2: Atmospheres

PREFACE: INNOVATION?

WHY INNOVATION NOW?

We live in an era of large-scale radical transformations from Black Lives Matter to Climate Change to rapid technological breakthroughs — all of which exceed the grasp of our existing conceptual, social, ecological and political tools.

To truly engage with these and other novel changes we need new tools — for it is our historical tools, structures and habits that have gotten us into this reality and are unlikely to get us elsewhere.

We need innovation to help us break with what has been done — we need to imagine that the future does not need to mirror the past with only minor corrections. Today, more than ever, we need the powers of creativity and invention to open up the possibility of genuinely new futures.

That is one clear reason. For us there is another just as important and valuable a reason for becoming innovative and engaging creativity: wonder.

We live in an open and evolving universe full of creativity and ever advancing into novelty. Innovation ultimately does not "solve" anything — it coaxes transformative differences to emerge and these differences in turn change us and the world in astonishing ways.

Living actively within and of a world of change is to live in beauty and adventure. With this foremost in mind, think of creativity and invention as fundamental skills for being alive, for the flourishing of life — it is what allows all of us collectively to make new and meaningful changes in our precarious and ever changing reality.

The practices of creativity and invention are fundamentally about developing a sense of joy, curiosity, and agency within the changing nature of reality that exceeds us at every moment.

HOW?

This is no easy task: between the potential to simply improve on the past and the space of novel possibilities is an infinite qualitative gap.

Novel futures *necessarily* exceed knowing and first come into being not as something we can recognize and fully grasp *but as vague and amorphous new modes of doing, making, sensing, and feeling.*

This is the paradox of radical creativity. We can know an issue extremely well, but the new, to the degree it is truly new — *cannot be known in advance.*

This book and its approach are grounded in this paradox. Both because of this paradox, and the very real challenges we face, we need new speculative tools for qualitative transformations — we need to be able to invent problems worth having for worlds worth making.

Other worlds are possible. This is both the genesis and goal of this text.

leave
space
for the
unexpected
to sweep
you
elsewhere

USING THIS BOOK

We have named the set of tools and procedures that we outline in this book *The Innovation Design Approach* (or IDA for short). IDA is a way of approaching creativity, invention/innovation and design in general. It is an ethos, an overarching framework and a set of connected practices for producing truly novel outcomes.

It is intended to be pragmatic and applicable across a wide variety of fields from ecology to entrepreneurship, from philosophy to politics, and from basic education to advanced biology. The core focus of the Innovation Design Approach is to help you develop processes that allow for genuinely novel possibilities to emerge in the face of difficult and open-ended areas of interest.

At the heart of our ethos is our conviction that ideas only come about from doing. Reading and ideating alone do not lead to novelty. Thus, we have written a workbook and not a textbook.

For creativity to happen this book needs to be used and not simply read, and it is with this in mind that we invite you to see the purpose of this workbook as being twofold:

1. To help and teach you the key skills and tools for innovation (where our techniques act like a temporary scaffolding); and...

2. To support your unique innovation process no matter what phase of the process you are in.

A couple of additional thoughts:

1. As a learning tool this book is best thought of as a form of scaffolding designed to support and catalyze your learning, and because of this we do not attempt to cover every aspect or every skill needed for innovation. Our goal with this workbook is to give you a sense of the terrain and teach you a set of critical techniques and processes. Ultimately, as your skills develop the scaffolding is left behind.

2. Whatever stage of innovation you are in, we designed this workbook to help you. None of us are starting in the same place or facing the same issues. After the introduction we have a guide: How to Hack the Innovation Process, to help you figure out where to start in this workbook and how to proceed.

3. *On being practical & creative:* our goal is to assist you in experimenting collectively with the real so that the genuinely new emerges. As such our approach is entirely pragmatic. Why does this matter when redefining creativity? Being pragmatic, for us, means that all of our various claims and propositions about creativity and innovation are not intended as the ultimate definitions or final truths on the subject — but as useful tools and lures towards an experimentation that "excludes nothing" as William James puts it. Our goal is creative actions.

That said — pragmatism is never simple — in fact in regards to creativity pragmatism needs to be skeptical of the desire for simplicity. Things are just too surprising. The philosopher who coined the term creativity, A. N. Whitehead puts it well: *seek simplicity and doubt it.*

It's not that we want to make things complicated — far from it, but *change is never simple* -- it is always deeply strange and truly confounding. The pragmatism we are espousing is one of falling in love with change such that radical surprise becomes a given — *wonderment.* Being pragmatic in regards to creativity is to embrace the beauty and a joy of aberrant leaps and qualitative shifts. For us being practical and creative means that we need to care for beauty, joy and strangeness that is fully part of the practice of change.

For us, the Innovation Design Approach is part of an experiment to develop better tools and frameworks for innovation. As such, this book is an open toolkit which we hope you will experiment and *hack* freely. This framework's utility can be judged by whether it works for you.

How will you know if it works? Try the practices, do they lead you somewhere interesting? In doing so, we hope that you will change these practices and make them your own.

So try things out: experiment and evolve things and if you like what you discover in your experiments, be in touch, share what you discover -- let's continue this experimental journey as partners.

However you proceed, please don't ignore the glossary: while we strive to use simple everyday language, there is a downside to this: we need to use common words in very specific and occasionally odd ways. The glossary is meant to help clarify our tools and concepts (there's also an annotated bibliography that connects you to others.

REMINDERS AS WE BEGIN:

- Get out in the world, work with many others

- Ask yourself – what area do you wish to make a difference? Find similarly minded rebels, conspirators and collaborators. Put the book to work

- The great joy of invention is that you will change your practices, habits, outcomes and ideas many times. Welcome the change. Embrace it with a pen, pencil, eraser, extra paper, scissors, and glue. Cut, paste, erase, remake.

- Develop and transform the workbook. If something is not quite right for your project — that is a good thing. This workbook is meant to be transformed. Treat it only as a starting point and scaffold.

- Be playful, curious, malleable, and open to wonder.

- Pause, slow down, don't immediately jump to answering the questions. Take your time, read carefully, go out into the world, engage others deeply, ask questions, and make lots of notes.

- If the question does not apply or seems wrong, revise it (if possible never truly skip a question).

- Do things in order. Things build upon things.

- *Do not focus on solutions* (this will only lead you away from innovation). If you already know where you want to end up — then there will be no innovation. Focus on the process. Let the solution reveal itself to you through the process.

- Innovation is recursive, this means that you need to go backward and repeat steps more than once. Don't see this as a setback, it is the only way forward (really sideways — which is the new forward). If something is not working go back to the point where it was, and start again.

- To get good at innovating we feel strongly that it is most helpful to apply these tools to as many aspects of your everyday life as possible. Try them at differing speeds and with differing intensities, set yourself short challenges: could you cook a meal using this process? How about design a coat?

Repetition is an amazing teacher: make hundreds of meals and thousands of variations of your daily habits.

- Enjoy the process, don't prejudge outcomes, fall in love with what you don't yet understand, be moved by things. Laugh, care, and be curious about what changes you.

- Be in touch.

everything begins and lives in the middle

ON INNOVATION

PART ONE: IT'S TIME TO REINVENT INVENTING
In the Beginning was the Detour

Before we begin engaging directly with innovation and creativity we need to pause and take a detour into the early history of these concepts in the West.

Really? Why?

(Yes, we get it, why revisit ancient history, when we are trying to get to the future! But, there really is no other way...)

We Have Nearly Everything Wrong About Creativity

If we go back and uncover the logic of the early history of creativity we will see that as a culture we have nearly everything wrong about creativity.

We don't say this lightly or for the sake of being provocative. This is a conclusion that we have reluctantly come to through our work over the last two decades helping communities, academics, individuals and companies innovate across a crazy diversity of fields, contexts and situations globally.

Searching for a Method

Years ago, when we first started working with others to innovate, we would spend countless hours researching, testing and modifying dozens of existing ideas, approaches and systems for fostering creativity — we tried pretty much everything from Human Centered Design to Lateral Thinking and much else.

*It was only through utilizing and putting these innovation approaches to the test that we came to seriously doubt all standard models of creativity, design and innovation. Quite simply they did not lead to innovation — at the most, they led to reasonably interesting variations of what we already knew. But, *real* innovation? No.

It must be something in the Water

Seeing firsthand the limits of so many highly distinct models for creativity led us to realize we needed to look deeper into how we as a culture have come to define, understand and conceptualize creativity.

Creativity is not part of the Western Tradition

Digging into the history of creativity in the Western tradition was, for us, at first profoundly frustrating, and ultimately a transformative experience that revolutionized our own approach to innovation.

What was really frustrating was *the total lack of any discussion about what we would call creativity* (the making of something genuinely novel). Going all the way back to the ancient Greeks there is simply no discussion of how humans can make something novel.

The West always understood Creativity as Copying

Instead what we found was a model of making via *inspiration.* Inspiration literally means: "divine guidance." Human creation was understood as following a pregiven model (God's plan) gained via inspiration (God's help), which we should then copy and make it real as best we could (God's grace). In this framework, we humans come to do novel things only by following a directive stemming from a fixed plan gained by outside intervention.

Truth is Antithetical to Creativity

What was the content and goal of this divine guidance? From these ancient Greek beginnings, divine guidance (the muses) took the form of assisting us in uncovering a predetermined and ahistorical ideal (idea and plan).

These ideals were manifestations of *true* essences (pure ideas). And for the Greeks to be true meant it could not be *changeable* — after all two plus two cannot equal five tomorrow and still be true. Truth was something fixed and unchanging. Because it was unchanging it could not be material, tangible or part of our everyday world — for everything material in this world eventually decomposes and disappears. In the world of our everyday lives, everything changes. Thus the ideals — the essences and truths that the western tradition sought to uncover and follow were necessarily immaterial, unchanging, essential truths. And as unchanging truths they reveal a mindset in which the highest human aspiration is not in making something new or of this world but in copying perfectly something unchanging and otherworldly.

Creativity: Find and Follow the Plan

Western makers and thinkers came to see fixed essences and unchanging models everywhere. This search for hidden plans and models behind everything can be seen in Da Vinci's famous *Vitruvian Man* sketch. Da Vinci believed that humans were necessarily modeled on perfect geometric forms of the circle and the square.

That one could define the human form with a circle, and a square showed that there was a fixed hidden plan and perfection to the universe.

While today we admire Da Vinci for what we understand anachronistically to be his innovations and inventiveness — in short his creativity — he understood himself to be doing the opposite: finding and following a timeless truth to the full degree his "genius" (the inclinations that God gave him) allowed him. For Da Vinci and the historical Western tradition, the world and all that is — is the physical realization of a pre-existing ideal or plan.

In this tradition, humans are always situated as more or less successful copiers of a pre-existing immaterial ideal or plan. Within this worldview, only God, or some form of prime mover, could be said to truly create something novel (in coming up with the ideal plan). Humans on their own do nothing genuinely creative.

Ideas are Everything

We are those who gain access to the "mind of God." And then once we have access these ideas flow into our mind as ideas that we can act upon.

Same Pattern Different Time

It would be a mistake to think of this as simply a religious worldview, or an outdated mode of philosophizing, or a quaint, but interesting, historical anecdote. The underlying logic of this story is still very much the underlying logic of how we understand and explain the invention of things and the functioning of scientific truths.

- Everything begins as a pure idea
- It is immutable and immaterial

- This idea acts as a plan
- Carrying out these ideas as predetermined plans is how everything comes into being
- Making is reducible to the simple act of carrying out the plan
- Making is the imposition of form (the idea) on passive matter

Once you recognize this model, you will see it is everywhere:

- Physicists speak of knowing the mind of God when they discover a fundamental equation — even going so far as to imagine the existence of a singular unified theory of everything (The Plan) — that one equation that could explain everything.

- Artists and inventors talk of having a eureka moment when the plan comes to them in a single moment of vision.

- Geneticists talk about genetics as the hidden plan inside each cell that the cell follows to make the next cell based upon the genes predetermined model.

There can be no doubt that this model is very much alive and well today.

But is it the correct way to understand creativity and reality in general? Does it have any actual validity?

The simple answer is no — it is based upon outdated concepts of (1) an unchanging and closed universe, and (2) novelty springing from human minds.

Despite this knowledge our historical habits persist — we are still mistakenly looking for unchanging essences, fixed mind-based ideas and complete blueprints — and in doing so fail to see how the reality all around us is complex, highly interdependent, historically contingent, planless, and profoundly creative — with novelty emerging spontaneously where least expected.

Creativity has only existed for 150 years in the West

In light of this, it makes perfect sense that the very first usage of the word "creativity" in English as a noun was only in 1875. While this might sound shocking, it is profoundly important to recognize that *we do not come from a history or tradition that has had a longstanding interest or place for genuine novelty.* And because of this, most of our contemporary ideas about creativity carry over complex hidden anti-creative habits, concepts and processes.

Our models of Design & Making are Unwittingly Ancient

The inability of our current creativity models to foster real novelty makes perfect sense when you realize that they have unwittingly carried over into the present the basic logic and process of a tradition that understands novelty as ultimately unreal or as only arising from some fixed ahistorical idea.

But, understanding this fixation with fixed ideas and plans does not fully explain the power these models have held over our development of creative methods. The main force that these models have today is in the *processes* that we still use to foster creativity. These historical models of design are "God models" and their process is one in which they ask us to act like a God of creation and *to think things into being.* This process has three key steps:

1. *Ideate*

2. *Plan*

3. *Make*

1. IDEATE   2. PLAN   3. MAKE

But, if creativity is, as we will argue, about the emergence of *anything* novel — how can it be focused on ideation and the follow-through from this initial idea?

Do new forms of life creatively emerge via ideation?

Of course not — how could a dinosaur brainstorm its way into becoming a bird? If we look around and see the novelty of life — we know that none of this creativity followed a plan or an idea — it came about because of a complex, contingent and unthinking process of evolution (which we will investigate shortly for cues to an alternative model of creativity).

With most of our current models of creativity, we can see that they have unconsciously carried forward the classical linear model (ideate, plan, make) that never had to actually address the question of how novelty is possible because it was taken for granted that God alone created.

But with God — or any fixed immaterial ideal — removed from the picture of creativity, does this linear model still make sense?

How does this "ideate first" model account for the emergent creativity that arises in action? In materials? In environments? In evolution? In unplanned accidents?

Before fully addressing these questions that take us into the heart of real creative processes, it is important to understand how pervasive and implicit this "ideate first" model of creativity is today.

In our own research and comprehensive surveys of models of creativity — nearly every model assumes that creativity is about thinking and ideas (we will mention the rare alternatives later).

Classical creativity and design are taught as a process of developing an idea, drawing it up (as a plan to show how to make it) and then making it (or have it made).

Go to almost any design or architecture program today and you will see students presenting perfectly rendered ideas and plans for feedback.

Pick up pretty much any guide to innovation and its process will begin with Ideation.

Aren't we being far too all-encompassing? Are there not

examples of design processes that do not begin with Ideation? For example, doesn't Design Thinking begin by empathizing and talking with users?

This is true, but the revisions to this process proposed by Design Thinking and other similar models keep the core model intact and simply tack on an extra step at the beginning. For example:

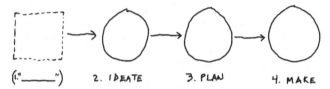

- Design Thinking adds Empathy
- Jeremy Gutsche adds Trend Analysis
- Equity Centered Community Design adds history and context
- Disciplined Entrepreneurship adds a customer focus
- Frame Innovation adds Frame Research
- Lateral Thinking adds techniques to loosen thinking
- The Innovators Dictionary adds analysis
- The Radical Innovation Playbook adds discovery

We encourage you to look at every innovation design method — the vast majority are basically "Ideate Plan Make"?

You will be surprised, *there really is not much else...*

While all of these tools (empathy, trend analysis, frame research, etc.) are critically important to good design — tacking these onto the fundamentally flawed skeleton of the model still leaves you with a fundamentally flawed model.

Yes, But what's the Flaw?

What is it that makes this three-step "ideate first '' model so problematic for creativity? After all one could argue that its origin is beside the point — if it works to produce novelty.

If it works, does it really matter if it was invented as a myth?

So the question is: can the "ideation first" model produce profound novelty? There are three fundamental problems that sink this ship:

1. Thinking does not actually happen in the head: On Ideas and the mind of God

If we pause for a moment and just reflect on how creativity models are focused on ideation — it is in the literal dictionary definition of creativity. The Oxford English puts it this way: Creativity: *"the use of the imagination or original ideas, especially in the production of an artistic work"*.

What is important here is (1) ideas are where creativity begins, and (2) ideas — thinking happens in the head.

So we are looking for a brain region?

The now almost universal assumption is that of course thinking happens in the brain and therefore we should move onto narrowing down the hunt for the source of creativity to its specific location (or locations) in the brain.

This "it's all in the head" model with its brain region focus for understanding activities like creativity has also underpinned most of the classical creativity research programs. This has led to a focus on creativity being something fundamentally neurological — a thing that can be strengthened or weakened by our habits and practices.

But, the most recent work in cognition and neurology does not support this approach:

1. The work of Michael Anderson and others on what they call "neural reuse" has definitively shown that the brain is not modular (one task - one area), but rather tasks such as seeing or speaking are widely spread across the brain and that these same areas

of the brain are utilized for a huge diversity of other tasks that have nothing to do with seeing or speaking. The dream of discovering a brain region devoted exclusively to anything — much less creativity — is thus an impossible dream.

2. An even more challenging development comes from the field of Embodied Cognition: thinking cannot be properly said to occur in the brain.

What? How can that be? Where else would thinking happen?

Thinking is outside the head

Of course, *our* type of thinking *requires* a brain, *but the brain alone is not sufficient for thinking.*

The brain is best understood as being functionally *inseparable* from the body-in-action interacting with the immediate environment.

Thinking does not take place in the brain — to properly understand thinking (and by extension, creativity) we need to understand that thinking happens via a coalition of brain-body-tools-environment.

The Four E's

This approach is based upon the discoveries of the Embodied Cognition (EC) approach to mind, brain, and cognition strongly critiques the classical "ideas = representations = brain processing" model of understanding thinking.

This can be understood as the coming together of how we are *embodied, extended, embedded, enactive and affective.* This is often called the "4EA" model of cognition for short (Embodied, Embedded, Extended, Enactive & Affective Cognition).

Let's understand each of these concepts individually:

1. Embodied: Our brains are part of our unique bodies. Having the types of bodies we do — moving, grasping, sensing, and acting with specific bodies gives rise to our forms of thinking which in turn feeds back into the forming of our bodies' abilities. Practically, what does this mean for thinking? The specific types of bodies we have, and how we use them directly shapes the underlying structure of our thinking — from guiding metaphors to abstract concepts. Changing the body and changing the body's habits/actions will change how you think.

2. Extended: The kinds of thinking that we do could not happen without tools. An example: most complex math is not possible without tools: writing (symbols) plus paper and pen, or chalkboards and chalk. Today our smartphones act as extensions of our memory storing hundreds of phone numbers we otherwise would not know. In thinking the appropriate set of partners are assembled: diverse brain regions + specific embodied actions + necessary external artifacts, into a holistic coalition to carry out the task of thinking. Again, practically, this means that to think creatively we need to focus on new tools, techniques, and practices and connect them experimentally into effective novel *assemblages*. We can think of this as setting up types of labs for novelty. Tools/objects will surprise us with unintended capacities that can be discovered and followed under the right conditions.

3. Embedded: Thinking is embedded in a concrete environment and this environment shapes and patterns thinking. Chairs, rooms, houses, streets, and patterns of sidewalk and lawn might seem incidental but are fundamental not simply to thinking in general but to why our thinking gravitates towards certain patterns, logics, and outcomes.

4. Enactive: Thinking is fundamentally tied to acting — to doing where meaning arises via our actions. Meaning and thought arise during situated actions that are in a context of being co-determined along with our environment. Doing en-acts meaning into being. A cup is a cup because we use it as a cup (for containing liquids to drink), and the idea of containing arises through our specific actions of using things like cups to contain as part of a larger action such as drinking — which in turns gives rise to a model of quenching thirst which gives rise to a conceptual terrain of "thirsting" and being "quenched" — that extends far beyond actual liquids and physical needs.

5. Affective: We equate thinking with rationality, logic and high-level conceptualizing. While we do use logic — our intellectual lives and all of our thinking rests upon an emotional foundation that is continuous with, colors and saturates all experience. Experience and thoughts bubble up out of an emotional atmosphere — tone — that is our most basic sense of being alive. Most of the time we are not even aware of this emotional (affect) shaping our thoughts — emotion is working at a subconscious and minimally conscious level. And then when we are called upon to explain our actions or thoughts we skip right over the role of emotion and jump right to "reasons and logic" most of which have little to do with the actuality of our experience, decision making or thinking. Understanding this is critical to creativity and we will go into this in detail in the next section.

How does all of this help us be creative? Anderson says it best, "we are [embodied] social environment-altering tool users. Tools give us new abilities, leading us to perceive new affordances, which can generate new environmental (and social) structures, which can, in turn, lead to the development of new skills and new tools, that through a process… of scaffolding greatly increases the reach and variety of our cognitive and behavioral capacities" (Anderson, p. 182).

And this is far removed for a world of brainstorming and other techniques of pure thinking and ideation — which is very good, because:

2. The new is unthinkable: The Creativity Paradox

Here is where the central problem lies with ideation first models of creativity: the modes of thinking that ideation relies on are high concept and representation dependent. They are most often inductive or deductive forms of conceptual reasoning. And these concepts pre-exist the activity of ideation and fundamentally shape it. Ideation is thus inherently tied to the past and what already exists. And if it already exists it cannot be considered to be novel, which means: *ideation cannot directly lead to novelty.*

Ideation, and thinking in general, is by its very nature a fundamentally conservative activity.

Put bluntly: if something is genuinely novel it cannot at first be conceptualized. Radical novelty at its birth is a-conceptual and non-representational. Humans cannot independently think their way to the new, therefore the whole Western edifice of three-step "ideate first" model of developing novel outcomes falls apart: starting with, and focusing on, ideation will never lead to genuine novelty. And moving through a linear sequence of Ideate, Plan, and Make is logically antithetical to creativity.

Does this mean thinking and idea generation have no role in creativity? Of course not. Ideas matter. But it is a question of when, in what form, and in relation to what other ongoing activity. We like to say:

No Ideas But in Making.

But that's just the beginning of it. Now let's turn to the

third fundamental reason our classical model of Ideate, Plan and Make cannot work:

3. Reality has a life of its own
It is not only ideation that is the problem. The process of three steps of Ideate, Plan and Make — and their sequence is deeply flawed.

First, these methods put all the emphasis on creativity as occurring solely at the initial stage of Ideation (after which you are just making the creative idea real via a plan and method of production). We now know that ideation cannot lead directly to novelty, thus having a model in which after novelty is ideated all that is left to do is "carry it out" will certainly never get to a genuinely creative outcome.

But, I Ideate, Plan and Make all the time!

Now, of course, you can have an idea, develop a plan, and make it real. That is not in doubt. We all do this every day:

I have an idea for a cup of coffee every morning, I make a quick plan to boil water in a kettle and grind some coffee, get a filter and make my coffee. No big deal: Ideate, Plan, Make.

But the question is: will this process get you anything creative and novel?

My idea to have coffee, and the carrying out of this plan travels a highly developed and far from the novel path. We cannot confuse a process that works in everyday life to simply get known things done with the process to get anything realized.

From the perspective of creativity, this process which puts all creativity into the first step of ideation and then relegates to the rest of the process the mere realization of the plan makes the fatal error of *assuming that the world is passive and has no creative impact on our designs*.

All creativity collaborates with the agency of things and environments

The classical way we tell the stories of great inventions and the emergence of new creative practices is to talk exclusively about the people involved, their ideas and their struggles. But almost nothing is said about the objects, materials, tools and environments involved.

Equipment of all kinds has surprising powers to shape outcomes and plays a fundamental role in innovation. What do we mean by "powers"? Put simply we mean that *things shape us.*

Contemporary studies of cognition have shown that the objects (and environments) we use, fundamentally shape and transform our thinking. Tools and their use rewire our brains, change our muscles and skeletons, remake our organs, make new patterns of thought, change our sense of self, and as Marshall McLuhan argued "leave no part of us, or our culture, untouched or unchanged."

Objects don't merely support or extend existing human capacities but *fundamentally transform us*: we are what we use. Obvious examples: how smartphones have transformed us, less obvious but perhaps more profound are the tools that we almost never notice such as our alphabet.

This is not an argument critiquing technology, far from it — *to be human is to use things* — *lots of things* and these things that we make and then use change us and this has always been the case. What matters is that we recognize that the things we make in turn make us, this is especially critical as innovators — we are not merely making things that solve problems but we are always making new things that change us and our surrounding environment to such a degree that new worlds emerge.

If creativity is not all about ideas or reducible to the human then we have to turn to *things as our partners in experimentation and invention*: *Making is thinking* when we allow things and environments to shape us as we shape them. In experimenting (as well as puttering, playing, tinkering, improvising, etc.) the agency of things comes into play:

When a carving knife meets a piece of wood, the wood — its uniquely organized form of matter — tells us things: I will split along the grain, I can bend, if you do this I will snap...

It is in this meeting space of action that vague hunches form: "what happens if...?" Here a kernel of an idea forms out from the midst of acting and it leads on to follow the material and the practices further. Vague thoughts form in making: no ideas but in making — and these nebulous thoughts do not act to impose plans from on high but ask us to experimentally stay in the messy mix of things and follow an emerging practice in which other ideas might emerge. Who is having these thoughts? *They are authored by the event.*

The "idea first" model of creativity and innovation imagines that matter is something passive, that in a God-like manner forcefully shapes a semi-arbitrary matter into whatever we imagine and deem it should become. But matter, stuff, things – have never been passive. Matter has propensities that come to the fore depending on how we engage with them and in this way form (what we want something to become) cannot be separated from the forming power of things as processes (splitting, bending, cracking, hardening, swelling, etc.).

The history of human invention shows us that most often the so-called great inventors were not great intellectuals purely ideating their way to novelty at a desk — they were most often the opposite: skeptical self-taught tinkerers who were most comfortable collaborating with materials and letting vague aesthetic feelings lead towards the emergence of speculative imaginings via experimental forms of deeply engaged probing, testing and making.

They experimented and noticed that wood if steamed bends along its grain. Metal heated and then quickly cooled will be far harder than a metal left to cool naturally. Add the mineral Kaolin to clay and it will become almost as hard as rock when fired.

When we do things with things they come alive and speak by revealing emergent properties.

Experimental engagement and not abstract ideation.

Rather than complaining about uncooperative makers and the right material not existing and retreating to pure visionary ideation — novelty emerges from the middle of puttering, playing, testing, experimenting, probing, noticing, and following.

This is not simply at the level of craft and object making — social change deals with systems far too complex and dynamic for any form of linear action to work. In complex systems, outcomes are by definition unknowable. Probing, following, coevolving and emerging are the only possibilities.

It can be argued (as we will later in this text) that all creativity comes from reality resisting our ideas. All human creativity surfs and takes advantage of some unintended (non-ideated) possibility of action (a plan)

So why are we not designing for and with the unintended?

After all, evolution does...

Why are we not working with things, environments and communities directly?

So, in a nutshell:

What is so wrong with our classical models? For us, there are six fundamental errors to the western model of creativity.

The six errors:

1. Creativity is practiced as being fundamentally about ideas and ideation

2. Creativity is developed as a linear process (even if it loops occasionally)

3. Creativity is envisioned as something that has an

essence and that can be reduced to a moment (Reductionism/essentialism)

4. Creativity is instantiated as the imposition of a predetermined form on a passive matter

5. Creativity is defined as primarily a human capacity

6. Creativity is understood and researched as an internal brain state

There is much to say about these errors and we will get into them as we articulate an alternative vision of creativity.

But this is getting ahead of the story, once we came to recognize these debilitating errors we saw them everywhere — and we came to realize that almost every contemporary method for creativity exhibits more than a few of these errors. This should come as no surprise as these concepts hang together as a package. They form our implicit unquestioned paradigm of creativity: this is the human-centered, brain-based, ideation-driven, anti-process, and anti-materialist paradigm of creativity that we in the West have inherited from an almost three thousand-year tradition.

Yes, it is not a simple or recent error — even a superficial glimpse at the literature on creativity will lead one to see that these are deep long-held widespread views encompassing the Western traditions going back to the classical Greek and early Christian thinkers. We have some deep — really deep habits that we have to work our way out of, as we build new habits of creativity.

We Require a Wholly New Approach to Creativity

To us, in light of these realizations, it is quite clear that today much of how we as a culture understand creativity and innovation seems profoundly misguided.

The point of this critique is not about getting history right or critiquing others — the goal is to pragmatically and effectively understand and foster creativity and ultimately powerful and necessary innovations. To do this we need to understand that part of why creativity is so hard to enact and to teach is *because we are still implicitly using anti-creative models, frameworks, concepts and assumptions*.

In our own work, we have come to learn the hard way that our historical Western paradigm of creativity *is anti-creative* and based on a series of false assumptions about reality, ideas, humans, brains, the world around us and creativity itself. For us, the consequences of these fundamental errors mean that we require a wholly new approach to creativity.

Challenging the Western Paradigm

Now, lest we give a false impression: it is not that these models have not gone unchallenged, in fact, there are alternative concepts -- the issue is that these alternatives are not part of the mainstream discourses of design, innovation or creativity. To develop new approaches to creativity and innovation one has to wander far from the usual haunts of design and creativity.

Our own deep frustration with the historical western model of creativity led us to work with researchers in a wide variety of fields. We worked with evolutionary theorists, systems thinkers, embodied cognition researchers, ecologists, urban planners, complexity scientists, non-Western philosophers and practitioners, material science researchers, social activists, political scientists, anthropologists, and historians. We know from:

- *Embodied Cognition* that our brains are neither disembodied nor idea centric

- *Evolutionary Theory* how creative novelty emerges across all life via the co-option of unintended potentialities

- *The Material Sciences* that there is a profound level of agency in all things

- *Process Philosophy* puts creativity at the heart of all existence

- *Complexity Science* that novelty can emerge in irreducible manners from systems themselves
- *Non-Western Traditions* that there are many important alternatives

While our doubts and frustrations led us to connect with researchers in a wide variety of fields to try and understand why these models did not work — we still had to develop alternative concepts and practices. After many years, we have slowly, via trial and error, come up with a handful of powerful alternative approaches. With every passing year and every new project, we have tried collectively to evolve these techniques and propositions further. This work on an alternative model of creativity has led to this set of alternative propositions for creativity.

What is creativity?

To begin we need a working definition of creativity. Let's start really simple:

Creativity involves the emergence of novelty.

Now novelty might sound like a trivial word, but novelty means that something new has emerged, and this is profound. The new is different.

Newness is achieved when something genuinely different than what previously existed appears.

Creativity has two forms: Qualitative and Quantitative

Innovation and creativity are about doing something new. The new involves making a change from the past — a difference. But not all forms of change, difference or newness are the same. Most often when we encounter change it is a small change to something that already exists. Perhaps it is an improvement, a minor adjustment, or extension of its functionality. Making a car go faster or more fuel-efficient are examples of this. This type of "problem-solving," that makes something better, is a form of developmental change.

But, is all change of this kind?

No, things that are radically different are not simply improvements, they are entirely different and totally novel approaches to reality.

Thus we can say that there are two distinct forms of change:

1. developmental

2. disruptive

In philosophy, these two forms of change are referred to as:

- Change-in-degree

- Change-in-kind

- Change-in-degree is: incremental, developmental, quantitative, world expanding, and probabilistic.

- Change-in-kind is: rupturing, disruptive, qualitative, worldmaking, and possibilistic.

For innovation and creativity, what is important is that:

1. Each form of change is a totally different creature

2. Each needs a different approach.

Creativity involves a looping between Kind & Degree

While each form is quite distinct (qualitative vs quantitative), and each requires different techniques and approaches to be properly engaged — they are neither in opposition nor totally separate. All forms of change are connected in a type of double loop: push a quantitative/developmental change far enough and it crosses a threshold and becomes a qualitative/

disruptive change, and vice-versa: every qualitative/ disruptive change needs to develop incrementally to be fully realized.

For example, if you slowly and incrementally enlarge a coffee table, it will become a dining room table, and if you kept on incrementally enlarging this it eventually would turn into a simple open shelter. The incremental shift from coffee table to dining room table is a change in degree: we are still dealing with tables. But, when we continue enlarging a table and it becomes a shelter — now they are categorically and functionally totally different, one we sit at, while the other shelters us from the environment.

Thus we have *incrementally* crossed a category threshold and gone from a change-in-degree (the two tables) to a change-in-kind (tables to shelters). We diagram this by transforming our original drawing of two opposing arrows into a closed double loop. This looping two-directional diagram and logic underlies the Innovation Approach.

While that is a good start to understanding creativity as two forms of change or difference, we need to go further with this definition:

Creativity is the *process* of the new coming into being.

It is not enough to talk about outcomes — of changes in degree or kind — we want to know *how* to get there!

How we get there is via a process.

Creativity is about processes of change, the development of differences and the emergence of the new — that is creativity: the process of the new happening...

engaged
curious
speculative
collaborative
actions

PART TWO: REORIENTATION

With our newfound awareness of the pitfalls of our historical model of creativity, and a sense that a new way is possible — we can now begin to develop an alternative approach. This reorientation requires reframing creativity, developing a new conceptual understanding, and developing new practices.
Let's begin:

Creativity is a worldly event

When we talk in general about inventions and creativity most of us would assume we are talking about some*one* who came up with a great idea who invented something. *Why?*

There are two important issues that radically curtail and derail our understanding of creativity:

1. we assume that creativity is a human activity, and

2. that creativity is an individual activity.

Let's begin with this latter point. *Why do we assume that creativity is individual?* Why do we so quickly get to the point where we are asking *who invented this?*

In so many of our stories of creation and innovation we keep trying to discover the discreet origin, the singular source, and the ultimate *human* inventor, author, or maker — and it is only once we claim to have found this *singular source* do we begin our explanation of creativity and invention.

It's not about Individuals

Pick up any book on creativity and innovation and notice how we as a culture are forever talking about "creatives" — those heroic individuals, with their special brains, and their unique essences. From Archimedes to Steve Jobs there is always someone (and ultimately someone's brain) behind everything new.

There is a fatal problem with this approach of connecting complex creative events to singular (human) sources: *nothing is ever so simple*; we now know that

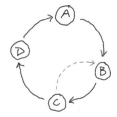

TWO LINEAR FRAMEWORKS

causality is not linear. In every moment and in every event countless factors and forces are involved in very unpredictable manners — and countless other possible outcomes could have happened. All of these factors are non-linear, indirect, contingent, emergent, multi-scalar, collaborative and irreducible. *Even the simplest moment of reality is a shit-show of complexity, and it is never possible to reduce this to a singular origin.*

NON LINEAR EVENTS

A counterargument is often made: yes everything is complex but only *that specific* individual at that specific moment had that idea — while many others were in similar circumstances but they did not come up with anything novel and therefore it must be something unique about that person. But, this is to both misunderstand and dismiss complexity and emergence: you cannot separate a person from all the other forces that collectively make up a unique event. It is the *holistic* uniqueness of the *event* and not the individual that gives rise to the outcome.

Once we realize this, we can take a pause on our ego-driven stories of creativity and invention. We can let go of the simplistic idea of linear frameworks and heroic individualism — they have led us totally astray for far too long. The closer we study inventions and creativity the more we will see that *things have no singular author, are not invented in one singular moment, nor stem from a founding idea*. Creativity is always the synergistic emergent outcome of a complex set of factors. This insight is a complex one based on many other insights: understanding emergence, how complex systems work, and the agency of things for example — all of which we get into in this essay.

Why does this matter?

Why does it matter that we put aside our heroic individualism and quest for singular sources?

To understand and more importantly *to be creative we need to be humble enough to see that no one "invents" anything or is "creative" separate from a complex messy world of forces that are just as much — if not more — the "author" than us*. And if we wish to be *involved* in

creativity we need to figure out how to work in harmony *with and become part of* this complex emergent association of forces.

Creativity is a more-than-human process

We can take this idea of a messy world of forces having untold emergent effects further: perhaps the most important and wondrous aspect of creativity and innovation is that *reality in all of its aspects is creative*.

Novel plants are evolving, whale songs are changing,

solar systems are forming, octopus intelligence is mutating, the Black Lives Matter movement is transforming how we develop city budgets, smartphones are rewiring brains, and slime molds are inventing totally new solutions to mazes. Everywhere we look creativity is happening.

Creativity and invention are not exclusively -- or even mainly, human practices (and certainly not simply psychological). The contemporary understanding of creativity needs to fully embrace this insight: Human-driven innovations emerge from within a reality where at every moment "something" is doing something wondrous and new *without an author or a plan*. We create in and with a world in which complex systems are spontaneously self-organizing, evolving and doing new and unique things at all scales. Bird wings and dragonfly wings are astonishing acts of invention and creativity, as are cell walls, and bacteria signaling...

The new bubbles up out of a chaos that haunts, overturns, and enlivens all forms of stable order.

An Interlude on Processes

Before moving on, let us dwell briefly on this all-important word: *process*. Far too much of how we talk about invention and creativity involves a heavy focus on things (outcomes) — nouns — and far too little attention to the dynamics of the situation: the coming into being and changing — processes and the unpacking of verbs.

Even the most seemingly stable of things — a hammer for example is a *process*: when we look at it we see wood and metal — two very solid and stable things. But, they too are dynamic processes: trees growing and minerals being pressed into forms deep within the earth for eons are processes. And from this tree the process of crafting and form giving to the handle is a process — equally the smelting and working of minerals into metals and hammering those into the head are processes. The hammer then goes to work — it is part of the processes of making — making with nails, planks, trained arms and eyes, homeowners with dreams, cultures with patterns.

If we zoom in further we see subatomic particles moving in relational processes, if we zoom out we see processes of building, and if we look to the side we see yet more processes of trees turning into planks, builders going to school, and much else besides.

In every direction, we see ongoing processes. To be attuned to creativity is to be tuned to change and *to be tuned to change is to feel and live processes*. Change happens and creativity happens because we change processes.

Creativity involves attunement to realities ongoing inventiveness...

Once we understand these intertwined concepts (creativity is a worldly more-than-human process) it makes no sense to talk of creativity as having a singular author, or being an internal human property.

Now, for many, this might feel interesting but beside the point — *"sure the world is also creative, but how are humans creative?"*

Which is a fair point, if creativity is an environmental and *worldly* phenomenon then our practices of creativity cannot be thought of as being in a separate realm. Human creativity is the skillful *participation in and collaboration* with dynamic systems and emergent phenomena.

Thus human creative practices are first and foremost processes of *active attunement and experimental engagement* with these complex worldly events of ongoing creativity. We are less the originators than the skillful joiners and participants in journeys that will shock all of us. To love and become actively creative is to shift our senses from a focus on the self, ego, or any one thing, to an emancipatory vision of ourselves swimming in, carried forward by and changing in response to a vast creative engaged open-world bubbling with inexplicable novelty.

Actual novelty, as we can see, challenges some of our most basic assumptions — challenging both who we think we are, what the things around us are capable of, how change happens, and where creativity is located in all of this.

If novelty and creativity are to be found everywhere in everything — then it is important to understand what we mean by "everything". To ask about everything is to ask fundamental questions about what is real, what is experience(d), and what counts. Reality is everything that has an effect.

What can it do? On affordances

COMMON CROW

TRAFFIC LIGHT

In our innovation workshops, one of the first things we do is show participants two pictures: one of a normal everyday nutcracker and the other is of a busy intersection with traffic lights and cars.

Then we ask them: *are these two things the same?*

At first, participants are hesitant to answer — the scenario has the set-up of a trick question, and who wants to fall for a stupid trick...?

But then the answers come:

"Obviously they are superficially the same — both are made of atoms", "Clearly they are designed for quite different purposes."

Both Yes and No could be correct answers.

But, we don't stop there:

Why would we ask such an obvious question at the beginning of an innovation workshop? What are we trying to get at by asking you this question?

From this prompt inevitably a participant will suggest some use or effect that the two things have: *they both crack things. One cracks other cars and the other nuts.*

And that's when things get interesting! One intentionally cracks things and the other unintentionally. If we ignore intentionality both have a similar effect.

Then we return to our original question: *are these two things the same?*

Which prompts a wormhole of semantics to open up. In the midst of this craziness, we show a new image: A crow sitting on a powerline.

It turns out that some crows use intersections to crack nuts. They use powerlines as perches, wait for the light to turn red and the cars to stop. They then swoop down and place nuts in front of the car tires, and then return to their perch. The light turns green, the cars crack the nuts, and then the light turns red and everything stops allowing the crows to descend and eat.

From the perspective of innovation, *it does not matter what something's identity or designated purpose is*, all that matters is: *what can it do? What does it afford?*

Be Like A Crow

It is more productive to not assign purpose, essence or identity to things but to look at what they can "afford" in relation to the situation.

Affordances are the emergent possibilities of a total situation. When cars, traffic lights, roads, trees, and crows come together in a specific manner the situation affords the crow the novel creative possibility of nut-cracking.

"Be like a crow": don't fixate on purpose, intentions or identity — rather start using things in novel ways to discover what all else they might afford. But don't stop at one possibility — keep experimenting to discover more and more non-intentional possibilities.

For us, becoming a crow is to realize that:

1. nothing is reducible to its seeming purpose or intention

2. the discovery of new possibilities can only happen through our experimental *use*.

Developing a way to "be like a crow" — a "crow becoming" so to speak is a critical first step of innovation.

From "what is it?" — to "what can it do?"

We, as innovators, are ultimately simply interested in affordances and effects and working with these to have a novel effect on something. We wish to judge things not by "what they are" in perfect isolation — but by what they afford and what effects they can produce in specific circumstances.

Not "what it is" — but "what can it do"...

But this never stops: "And what else can it do?" — This question keeps repeating as novelty emerges in experimentation...

And what all else is possible?...

Creativity works with any and all effects:

From this crow perspective into creativity, *reality is everything that has an effect.*

But what is a "thing" in this case when we say "everything"?

Is a rumor such a "thing"?

How about a delusion?

Are these the same as a hammer?

Or a political movement?

Of course, a delusion is different than a hammer — that is not in doubt, but is a delusion any less *real* for being judged untrue? While these are very different types of things (false ideas vs physical tools), *they all have equally real effects.*

If all of these effects lead directly to change — *why would we consider any of them less real or less important?*

Why does this matter?

If we begin thinking about creativity only after parsing out and ignoring most of reality because it could be characterized as merely subjective, or false we both miss how reality is and how we can have an impact on it.

The question needs to be "what can it do?" not "what is it and is it really real?"

The former question is an experimental one — it is about doing, testing, noticing, following, and ultimately creating the new.

The latter is about adjudicating reality from a distance — and this offers creativity nothing. Rather it continuously reinforces only what already exists and is well and properly defined.

Experience — that sense of what something is for someone in some context (the world of affordances) cannot be separated from reality.

Following William James, and his definition of radical empiricism, we propose an alternative starting point for defining the real from the perspective of creativity: "To be radical, empiricism must not admit in its constructions any element that is not directly experienced, *nor exclude from them any element from them any element that is directly experienced*".

Put simply, *reality is everything that has an impact.*

Experience both feeds back and feeds forward into reality.

For us as change-makers interested in creativity, this is where we begin:

We are not concerned with determining once and for all what is really really real — but only in determining what has an impact — what produces an effect — what some-thing affords — for everything that has an impact is precisely what is going to impact creativity and invention.

All "things" (objects, concepts, systems, habits, collaborations) have their own emergent transformative powers and *perspectives*.

Back to the Crows!

Creativity Surfs Unintended Possibilities

What Crows understand about how to engage with reality is also one of the secrets to all novelty: *The unintended is at the disruptive heart of all novelty.* It is no exaggeration to say:

All radical forms of creativity utilize the unintended possibilities of a system or a thing. A quick perusal of the history of human inventions bears this out:

- The computer: a knitting machine
- The Internet: Originally a closed communication system for the military.
- GPS: developed to track satellites
- Antibiotics: uncleaned lab equipment
- The lightbulb: the early filaments were threads, paper and bamboo
- Plastics: a shellac replacement for wood
- Viagra: a heart medicine

This list is infinite — every disruptive innovation involves the unintended. But it is not just human inventions that involve the unintended — all creativity from the big bang to the flight of birds is a story of unintended possibilities being activated. Given that things have agency to shape us, it follows that they also have unintentional agency to shape us otherwise than expected.

This is how we step away from the Creativity Paradox

If the first part of the answer to the innovation paradox is that creativity does not begin with ideas but highly engaged actions and vague feelings, the second aspect is that creativity does not require a pre-existing conceptual plan to be realized because *it begins with a radical act of repurposing a previously existing something for an unintended, and most often unrecognized, end.* This repurposing can be a simple functional shift or utilization of an unintended aspect of the design.

We see this repurposing most clearly in the biological evolution of features such as eyes, wings or feet. Neither feet, wings nor eyes initially evolved for their current use -- this use was an unintentional development arising out of a previous quite different use.

A classic evolutionary example of unintended shifts in function involves the story of how fish migrated from the sea to land. For this to happen fins had to evolve into feet. This has been a vexing question of Evolutionary Historians for quite some time. Originally it was thought that environmental changes propelled this process: water bodies were drying up and shrinking so for fish to survive the ones lucky enough to randomly have stronger fins would drag themselves between ponds. Slowly the environmental necessity to crawl on land propelled a change and bit by bit fins turned into feet while crawling on land.

This neat explanation turns out to be another false just-so story: feet do not finally emerge late in the story on land — feet evolved early in the story *in the ocean*. Who needs "feet" in the ocean? Clearly, they helped with swimming and many other non-walking activities. Feet-like fins are simply one of a vast array of aquatic propulsion strategies that emerged in the ocean.

Feet for swimming had the unintended capacity to do many things: they could help fish linger invisibly on the bottom and spring up to ambush prey, they could help fish navigate underwater grasses without giving away their location, and much else besides. Long feet and arm-shaped protrusions proliferated on diverse fish species along with other evolutions such as their eyes moving toward the tops of their heads (to see airborne flies).

But why go on land? There is no one answer, but we know with certainty it was not because of environmental change. One interesting possibility is the juvenile footed fish "escaped" briefly onto land to avoid predation and discovered they had unintended capacities to survive briefly out of water.

The french "detournement" — rerouting or hijacking is an ideal term for this *process*.

Detournement — It's a Process, Not a Concept:

While the general concept is critical, it is the detailed process that once understood abstractly can be applied to the development of a new innovation approach.

If we were to zoom in on this process we would see that it is composed of a series of pivots in purpose.

"Purpose is a Porpoise" (bpNichol)

Everything has a purpose in relation to someone doing something (an agent, an activity, and purposeful things). The traffic light is like this: if drivers are the agents and driving is the activity, then the traffic light serves the purpose of organizing the flow of traffic to avoid accents and keep things moving. But "hovering" around or "haunting" this purpose are infinite immanent and emergent unintended possibilities awaiting a literal realization and production in use. The crow does this and a new purpose emerges: nut cracking. But this is a one-time event.

Tracking our evolving fish, the story reveals a more complex process. A key aspect of the fish to land transition is the fin to foot transformation, and the heart of this is the story of the evolution of cartilage and bone.

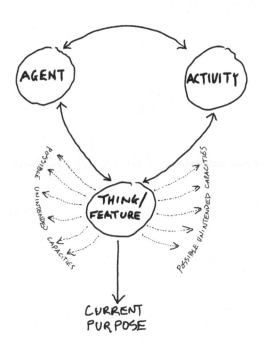

AGENT ←→ ACTIVITY

POSSIBLE UNINTENDED CAPACITIES

THING/ FEATURE

POSSIBLE UNINTENDED CAPACITIES

CURRENT PURPOSE

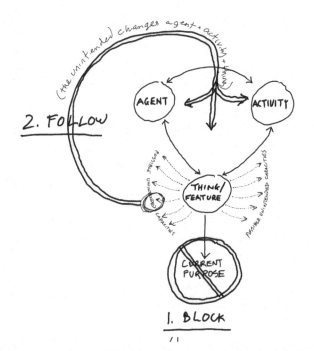

(the unintended changes agent + activity + thing)

2. FOLLOW

AGENT   ACTIVITY

POSSIBLE UNINTENDED CAPACITIES

THING/ FEATURE

POSSIBLE UNINTENDED CAPACITIES

CURRENT PURPOSE

1. BLOCK

Why did cartilage first evolve?

One might think it is obvious: to give fish structure. But, that is not the reason — in fact, that is the unintended outcome of what happened: cartilage first evolves to help sequester toxins that could not be effectively flushed out of early oceanic beings.

So, now fish have bones that unintentionally help them swim — what next?

Not so fast. The cartilage goes through various twists and turns to get to this point — essentially a series of these sideways movements of purpose being pushed aside by the unintended being discovered in action. There is no linear path here. Just a lot of branchings and many twists and turns.

But, we can skip ahead to fins?

Sure, by chance fins evolved in two directions: one type joined the body in a single spot (lobe finned), while most joined the body at more points (ray finned).

RAY

LOBE

Mutations diversified these designs and the variations allowed form unintended possibilities to emerge.

Many of these minor mutations of a lobe fin developed appendages that we would now recognize as "legs"

So the ocean was full of "legged" fish swimming around?

Sure, and it still is. Each of these leg-fins affords certain beneficial actions and each harbors unintended capacities.

It is not just about the fins right? Wouldn't you need lungs to breathe on land? A flatter body perhaps and eyes looking in the right direction?

Yes. Many other changes were going on in parallel.

Lungs surprisingly evolved quite early on and many early fish had both lungs and gills. It is believed that lungs are an unintended by-product of digestive "cough" reflex in primitive fish. In most fish lungs evolved into swim bladders because lungs were not necessary but had the unintended capacity to regulate buoyancy.

And fish bodies definitely varied and some larger fish developed longer slender bodies suited to stalking in underwater seaweed beds and tall underwater grasses.

Eyes moved towards the top of the head to help some fish eat airborne creatures like flies.

So we have many converging lines of unintended capacities?

Yes, and each of these lines consists of a long series of mutations making intended features and unintended features — and all of these features are being activated in novel ways over and over again.

And at some point land comes into play?

Well, yes — there was a leg-finned fish who enjoyed hunting in shallower plant-filled waters where their leg-fins gave them the advantage of both pushing off the bottom to ambush other fish and allowed them to stealthily swim through the grasses by gently pushing them aside with their leg-fins. They were quite big — over a meter but their young would regularly, perhaps at first accidentally find themselves on land in an attempt to escape being eaten. Now their leg-fins, lungs, arms, long bodies, etc. unintentionally afforded them new possibilities. Which at first must have been very modest — the ability for a few of them to push themselves back into the water when the chase was over. But eventually, a new feedback loop evolves between unintended capacities, their further mutations, new behaviors, and an environment that allows them to live on land. At this "moment" it would be right to say that a wholly new "world" emerges — the world of land animals.

So this is the process we could use for a new approach to innovation?

Yes, the sideways step-by-step process of detournement until a threshold is crossed from a change in degree to a change in kind. And then developing this novel world.

Is there a type of "blocking" going on in this process?

That's a critical part of all of this: Essentially at each step of the process the major purpose or affordance of a feature is ignored, or "blocked" as you put it — and a process is undertaken to discover what else it can do. This process of ignoring is a type of blocking or creative negation.

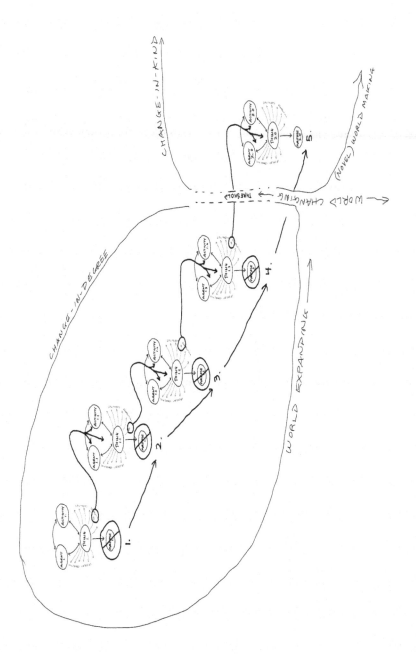

So this is what people mean when they say "break all the rules"?

Sure, it's a bit like that. You're experimentally breaking the "rules" for how something is used. But, just as importantly you are making new rules.

This new understanding of the process of evolution is of major importance to reinventing creativity and putting it on a surer footing. The process of evolutionary change — evolutionary invention really is at its core an emergent "purpose switching" of features via unintended capacities to entirely novel ways of being alive (from water life to land life).

In evolutionary theory, this process of utilizing unintended capacities is termed "exaptation". The term means "outside of aptation". Aptation meaning a feature that suits an organism to its environment. Exaptation is in contrast "adaptation" which is the further development of a characteristic to suit a creature to its existing environment.

Exaptation and Adaptation mirror the logic of change-in-kind and change-in-degree.

We can thus conceptualize the process of innovation as being composed of two distinct design logics: Exaptive Design and Adaptive Design. Exaptive Design is used to develop disruptive novelty, and Adaptive Design is used to improve something.

Exaptations and Affordances

We need to go down a seeming wormhole for a moment: what do we mean by "features"? An eye or a foot is a feature. A cup handle or a chair seat are also features. It is easy to think of these things as fixed, obvious, and objective.

But this is not the case. The cup handle is only a "handle" if you have a hand. It is of critical importance to innovation to keep in mind that *the features of things or creatures that we are talking about are not neutral, obvious or objective.*

Features only show up as what they "are" in action. (This connects back to our Crow — things or in this case features are what they can do in a certain context for a certain subject (the crow for example).

Features are relational.

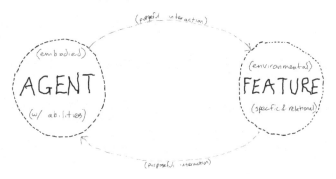

You cannot "see" them by being a disinterested neutral observer of reality — they only emerge in action or when following action (use).

A thing is its use. A feature is its use. A chair "seat" only exists for those who could sit in it — no spider or crow thinks of a chair as being a tool for sitting. Chairs don't show up for spiders or crows.

In regards to creativity, a better way to talk about features is with the term "affordances." This term, from ecological psychology, focuses on what the feature affords or allows (for a specific creature in a specific context). Thus a feature/affordance is best thought of as a directly sensed "opportunity for potential action".

Think of how often in the course of the day we use whatever is handy to do things: we step on a chair to change a bulb, or a dishcloth to grab a hot pan, or a large mug as a smartphone speaker. In these moments we see the world around us directly for what it *affords*.

Drawing upon what we just learned from evolutionary theory we can understand the world being composed of two types of affordances for any situated creature (an inventor for example): intentional affordances and unintentional affordances. And the process of innovation as involving the experimental ability to block one, and experimentally draw the other into existence.

What of Human Innovation?

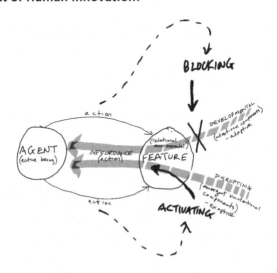

Exaptations are not limited to biological evolution; we see them in *all* innovations from GPS to the internet, to antibiotics. What is critical is:

1. This emergence of novelty from the unintended is an iterative process — one unintended possibility leading to another unintended possibility to another in a series of sideways moves and unanticipatedly leaps;

2. As such — there is no "creator" in the literal sense of the word, only a someone or some group that is experimental and attentive to a difference that might be important at the initial stages of creation. The interactions and the total agency of the system are critical. We collaboratively notice, foster, follow, nourish and stabilize...

3. Creativity and innovation happen in sensing, following and allowing oneself to be transformed by the unintended, such that novelty can emerge.

4. At some point, a threshold is crossed and a novel way of being alive emerges (a new world emerges). And this is what we are looking for when we pursue disruptive innovation: worldmaking.

Things both have a purpose and exceed their given purpose. And we as designers can improve the given purpose (developmental design, or adaptive design), or we could experiment towards radical novelty by ignoring, refusing or even *blocking* the given purpose as we follow unintended possibilities (disruptive design, or exaptive design).

To gain skill in exaptive design it is important to understand all the forms of exaptivity:

1. *Intentional Components with unintended but existing effects:* This is the form we come across most often. When we use a chair as a ladder, or a shoe as a wine bottle opener we are using an intentional feature for an unintended but existing purpose. Ladders and bottle openers exist. In this

way, we are not inventing a new purpose. Most often when we do this we are really developing an existing thing or purpose. But, in experimenting with things in this way we can often see a way it could leap outside of its current category of use.

2. *Intentional Components that no longer have a use:* A great example of this is HipHop using the turntable and record in new ways as a true musical instrument which led to the emergence of a new way of being alive. Blocking intention is a good way to artificially catalyze this process: what else can something do if we ignore its purpose? The modern tattoo machine is another example — it was an electric pen that no one wanted.

3. *Unintentional Components that are physical by-products:* In every physical object there are parts that directly contribute to the purpose and there are parts that are there simply as necessary by-products: The extra skin under a squirrel arm that could afford it the ability to glide. Or the classical example from architecture: the spandrel — it is a novel feature that comes about when you connect a dome to four columns. This is perhaps the richest resource for exaptive design.

4. *Unintentional Components that are chance by-products:* We find these often in nature: a random mutation that has no impact, but later is activated to do something entirely novel. Usually only noticed in activity. The use of the drip in painting by Jackson Pollock and others is a good example. A variation of this is accidents and failures. Sticky Notes — the glue that did not stick...

5. *Unintentional Components working in category:* Most often these novel unintended uses stay within their category (Pollock is still painting). This should not be seen as limiting their innovation: Pollock was filmed dripping paint onto canvases in a dancelike manner, which unintentionally led other artists to experiment with art as "action + chance" which developed into an alternative paradigm for art.

6. *Unintentional Components working across category:* Hummingbird feathers and flight being used to make bird calls: the unintended use leaves the category of movement and enters or develops a whole new category of expression. The Wright brothers using hip steering in bikes to develop steering in gliders. These potential world-making leaps are of critical importance to innovation.

ADAPTIVE (developmental - change-in-degree)

RELATIONAL FEATURE

INTENTIONAL COMPONENTS

NO LONGER USEFULL FEATURE

INTENDED EFFECTS

UNINTENDED EXISTING EFFECTS

INHERANT ALTERNATIVE EFFECTS (existing uses/features)

to alternative existing uses

[EXISTING COMPONENTS & EFFECTS]

EXAPTIVE (disruptive change-in-kind)

UNINTENTIONAL
COMPONENTS

...SING

NECESSARY
PHYSICAL
BY-PRODUCT

CHANCE
PHYSICAL
BY-PRODUCT
(invisible introduction)

IN CATEGORY
EFFECT

OUTSIDE
CATEGORY
EFFECT
"injections"

[NOVEL COMPONENTS & EFFECTS]

Affordance and Exaptation are critical, but...

The hard thing with developing a new framework for innovation is that there are so many equally critical concepts and each informs and transforms the others. We need to understand all of them — and all of them at the same time!

While understanding both affordances and exaptation goes a long way — it is easy to misunderstand these concepts. The big mistake is to imagine that affordances and exaptations are pre-existing things "out there" that just need to be discovered.

As innovators, a red flag needs to go off every time we hear the word *discovery*. If the genuinely new does not pre-exist (if it did it would not be the new) — then there is never anything "out there" quietly awaiting discovery.

The new emerges from the middle of "nothing"

Back to our paradoxes: the new cannot exist prior to it existing. It is not hidden waiting to be discovered. It is nowhere. It does not exist. So "where" is it?

Everything has to come from somewhere — unless it is a true miracle — but then we are no longer talking about what humans can do or science can explain.

Here is the paradox: From where does the new arise if it must arise from somewhere but that somewhere cannot already exist as the new?

(Just know, this hurts us too — paradoxes are painful.)

The Something from Nothing Paradox:

Put simply: how can we go from nothing to something?

The "something from nothing" paradox is intimately linked to the Innovation Paradox. As we discussed the ancient Greeks struggled deeply with how "something could come from nothing" and proposed the metaphysical answer that we in the West have relied upon ever since:

You can't really get something from nothing — there has to be a fixed beginning from which everything else emerges: reductionism. For something novel to concur, there has to already be something in some other realm or hidden inside things themselves that has always been there and that all creation follows (a pre-established plan).

This model has shaped the Western mindset for over 2000+ years. It is a mindset and model that has made us look everywhere for either a being that has pre-planned everything or for a hidden pre-existing plan inside each and every being. In a nutshell: Essentialism + Reductionism.

It is the mindset that meant creativity in the modern sense did not exist in western thought as a concept until the 1800's.

But this ancient metaphysical answer to the "something from nothing" paradox simply begs the question: *Then who made that being or original plan?*

We end up with the infinite regression that children are so fond of:

And who made God?

And who made that being before God?

And what was before that?

And on and on...

But, it turns out there is no need to begin with a pre-established plan or a pre-given essence to answer the paradox of something from nothing: we now know that order can spontaneously emerge from chaos, and that the new can *"emerge"* from existing systems while being irreducible to them. This concept of emergence has now been well studied by the field of complexity science.

Emergence in this technical sense of the term means that the novel property that "emerges" is:

1. Greater and distinct from the sum of the parts that made it, while also being:

2. Irreducible to these parts, and

3. Exhibit a relational holism

4. Emergent novelty can make its own parts (global to local influence).

5. Emergent properties are instantiations of an Emergent Process.

This concept of emergence is an *ontological* one, for it argues that this feature of irreducibility to being explained by components parts is not simply because of a lack of current knowledge about how things really work — but that there is actually something real, new and distinct that has emerged which is irreducible to its component parts.

Emergence is an example of a complex non-linear process that is non-decomposable, with many levels of feedback and operating in a semi-autonomous manner. A key aspect of emergent processes is that they are *irreducibly relational*. Evan Thompson describes emergent features in this way: "They are constituted by relations that are not exhaustively determined by or reducible to the intrinsic properties of the elements so related. These holistic relations do not simply influence the parts, but supersede or subsume their independent existence in an irreducibly relational structure".

There are many examples of emergence all around us -- that we are conscious beings -- is a classical example of emergence.

Consciousness is something that requires having a brain, but is irreducible to the brain, and it changes the brain.

Cultural phenomena are equally emergent — coming out of the relational totality of bodies, practices, implicit sensibilities, tools, environments and shared histories.

Why does this matter for creativity? We so often understand making as a process of addition. We add parts together and get a whole (Think of how we assembled things with Lego as a child). Here the parts make the whole and the whole can be taken back apart and each part can be analyzed to understand the whole. This is a reductive model of making.

PERTURBATIONS
&
RESPONSE

We can reduce the final product to the parts and the process. Cars can be built this way on a production line.

But the genuinely new does not come about in this additive and subtractive linear manner. Disruptive innovations — changes in kind are best thought of as types of dynamic co-emergent processes that harness and activate chaotic processes iteratively via techniques of blocking.

Here it is important to remember that chaos — actual chaos, is not a totally random phenomenon. Chaos is always tending towards and dissipating from brief moments of spontaneous novel order. This can be both activated and stabilized. This is what we see happening both in evolution (the fin to foot) and the development of new art movements (the drip to new paradigms of art).

Open engagement and the unintentional *interaction* of things spontaneously generate higher-level order. Interactions — relations between things, self-organize into semi-stable states. Our practices of making interact with these ongoing processes of the creative universe, transforming itself such that "our" innovations and creativity are systems level emergences.

At this point, we can bring back the concept that exaptive features are forms of radical novel affordances. Affordances are activity dependent relations between an agent and its environment that are irreducible to any fixed property of the environment. Exaptive affordances are the unintended relation potentials that only exist in their realization. Which is to say exaptive affordances spring into being as potential pathways for novelty via an emergent process. Exaptations are genuinely novel, context-dependent, and relational. Evolutionary exaptations in natural history are contingent — if you rewound the clock back to the period prior to fish coming onto land and then let evolution play out again — something totally different and equally radical novel could have emerged and we would never have come into being.

Creativity is Emergent

One cannot understand the universe or creativity reductively. To say that "novelty emerges" is to say something very particular. Emergence is dependent upon but irreducible to its component parts. Novelty emerges in a way that exceeds what preceded it. As such, creativity absolutely exceeds the known. We mean this in a fundamental sense, the pre-stateable laws and conditions of a situation are exceeded by the emergence of novelty. *Novelty cannot be known in advance.* Working with creativity means to work with the non-knowable (not simply because we are not smart enough or don't have a powerful enough computer, they are simply futures that are *not* knowable in advance). This universe is a spontaneously emergent self-organizing universe. Creativity is part of this emergence. The theoretical biologist Stewart Kaufmann says it well, "How can we not be stunned by the fact that the biosphere... and human cultural evolution are co-constructing wholes despite partial lawlessness? We are indeed, beyond the Galilean spell, into creativity and emergence, to the unknown mystery into which we must all live our lives."

This radically curtails the classical ways we work (via techniques of decomposition, getting to the essence, returning to the origin and gaining oversight). Things, while decomposable, are emergent wholes in which their parts exist because of and for the whole. All of our classical techniques work reasonably well to deal with closed systems and simple forms of causality — the probables of our lives — but not the possibles — the strange emergent novelties that are so disruptive. Emergence means that you cannot start at the end (with something like a version of your final idea) to be creative. All of our techniques of solution-driven design utilizing brainstorming and ideation miss this critical truth.

Reality is open, complex, non-linear, entangled, systemic, ongoing — and so are the most vexing issues we face today.

Today we so often as makers continue to assume a closed world of discreet things and problems that is ruled by simple forms of causality. It is the failures and limits of these classical ideas and techniques that have played a significant role in our current ecological crisis. A major goal of this text is to move us towards more resilient ethical models of ecological emergent co-making, this requires a fundamental shift in our thinking and practices and broader cultural mindset. This approach requires us to be a lot more humble, collaborative, experimental, embedded, and long-term than we are used to as contemporary makers.

We are blind and thoughtless in the face of the New:

If the radically new is exaptive and emergent it is nowhere till it begins to happen. Because of this foresight, prediction, trend analysis, and deep knowledge of the past will not be of any direct help. Radical novelty is ontologically new.

It is a truly shocking surprise.

Of course, it might make sense and be explainable in retrospect, but that does not help one in the middle of co-emerging with the new.

If we are blind and thinking is of little help — what's left? *How do we work?*

1. Creativity happens when all action is probing

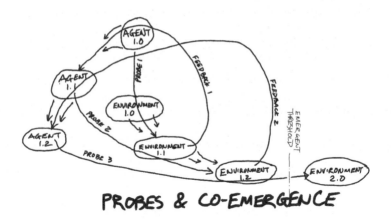

PROBES & CO-EMERGENCE

Reality, when looked at from the perspective of creativity, is simply too chaotic, dynamic, relational and emergent to gain a clear summative understanding.. If you try and pause things, and analytically pull it apart and understand the pieces all you will have is a narrow understanding of the pieces — but not the distinct but connected dynamic and emergent whole. Knowing root causes and developing predictive models will not work. So what can we do?

Probe.

Highly dynamic systems cannot be "understood" but we can perturbate them in specific experimental ways. The system will respond, and then we can adjust (both ourselves, our tools and our environment) and probe again. In this way, we are "making a path in walking it." We are attuning and transforming ourselves to make ever move successful novel assemblages emerge via a series of iterative probes and feedback/feedforward loops. This active probing involves developing exaptive tests (blocking & following). Like the fish, we will co-emerge with a new world (we, and our transformation, are never outside of the process).

2. If it cannot be thought, how does one think it?

Creativity is non-conceptualizable in its beginnings.

So, how does one conceptualize the non-conceptualizable?

We are always coming back to this: thinking is involved, we clearly cannot dismiss it entirely from the innovation process. But, we also know that the pathway to radical novelty cannot be centered on ideation (happening in the head/brain).

The way out of this paradox is not to develop better thinking techniques or mental exercises to make the mind more creative. The answer is strikingly simple: we can quite easily sidestep the paradox by realizing that creativity is the outcome of practices: *before we have an idea we are already doing something or making something or engaged in something novel that we cannot explain* and ultimately at this stage do not need to explain (if we could).

Before developing this, we need to reflect on the role thinking does and does not play in our everyday lives. You reach for your cup of coffee or walk across the room and sit down. You do not need to think through and plan out your every action and muscle movement. You reach for and drink from your coffee cup without much thought, just as you make it across the room and fall onto the sofa without any real thought.

Much of our lives involves a tacit "know-how" — we do

things — without requiring much — or even any "know-what" (complex thinking, knowing and planning). Many of the most skillful things we do — say rolling a kayak or breastfeeding are not things we could even put into words and explain without great effort. Often when we try to think about or articulate what we do in these nuanced practices we lose our way.

Thinking — knowing what — subsists upon and arises out of a far broader world of embodied and engaged know-how. The foundations of our lives, practices, values, and sense of being are ultimately unconceptualizable — it rests and thrives in action. Changing diapers, holding hands, serving dinner, watering plants, worrying when you see a police officer all ground our lives in ways that exceed ideation.

Innovation and Tacit Behavior

Engaged forms of play, puttering, tinkering, improvising, messing about, open experimentation, intentional stupidity, or curious observation while using novel tools in novel situations — are all common examples of how we sidestep the innovation paradox.

These are all examples of active open-ended experimental practices of *making and doing: probing*. Now what is critical in these practices is that we are doing two things: (1) making in a hands-on manner (at any scale), and (2) attending to the emergence of novel bodily sensations (affect) — feeling that something interesting, odd or curious is happening. This mix of open experimentation (doing) plus attending to differences that arise alongside vague *feelings* is a critical part of the beginning of the journey to making-discovering the new. Remember this is not the "kernel" of an idea -- the fish is feeling this directly as an embodied affect — and so too is a community.

At this delicate early moment of early doing-sensing, novelty can easily slip away, for it is not something we can recognize -- it is too new for that — in fact, we most often misrecognize it as a mistake — an error to be corrected. The mindset of play, tinkering, puttering, and probing are helpful precisely because they do not seek to overly conceptualize or judge. It is the rush to ideate that derails the early phase of the creative process.

As we openly experiment these feelings of difference are followed and our experiment takes on a heading as a feeling evolves into vague hunches arising through the force of the experiment itself (wayfinding). In activity, skills emerge alongside vague hunches, which lead one to follow a direction that slowly develops via intuitions, and swerving experiments into novel practices that only much, later on, are fully conceptualized as a new "idea".

Most of our lives are lived in this space of vague sensing and direct action. Clear and specific thought is a much smaller part of our daily lives than we imagine.

Emergent Wayfinding for Creativity

We can break down this process of emergent wayfinding into discrete steps for the sake of analysis (in reality they are far more mixed and continuously feedback/feedforward into each other). There are two phases:

1. Embodied Doing
2. Embodied Knowing

In the first phase knowing is implicit and tacit — the knowledge is non-articulable but exists directly in the emerging habits, practices and embodied skills, and vague feelings. Humberto Manturana terms this *"knowing-how without knowing-what"*. In the second phase these tacit forms of knowing slowly become articulable and eventually turn into abstractions that can stand on their own as fully-fledged concepts.

Emergent Wayfinding for Creativity:

PHASE ONE: EMBODIED DOING

(Know-how, Tacit ecologically distributed & emergent embodied abilities, open experimentation)

Making-Feeling: *sensing through making:*

Experimental doing-with (novel tools, environments and skills) and letting sensing-feeling tendencies vaguely co-emerge from *within* objects-in-the-making and return into the process. Joining resonances and tuning rhythms at an embodied/environmental level. Events arise and are stabilized when possible — these both take time and emerge as new forms of time. Vague sensations of "Interesting" and "puzzling" tendencies and events are felt and might rise to an intuitive level of attention. *Change is lived, but not represented.* Empathy.

Making-Dialoging: *thinking with making:*

MAKING – DIALOGING

Active following of an emerging form/tendency and responding (in the experiment): making-thinking with the emerging quasi-object crossing one or many thresholds (of capacity and stability). Signs act as triggers. Embodied skills, tools and practices co-develop in a back & forth between things and actions. Matter/things co-evolve forms immanent to the process. Non-conceptual know-how co-emerges with a "world-in-the-making" (concrete skills for repetition, expansion and discovery). We are living with things (as opposed to knowing things abstractly). Sympathy.

PHASE TWO: EMBODIED KNOWING

(Know-what, abstract conceptual knowledge, ideation of invention-discovery)

Thinking-Making: making with thinking:

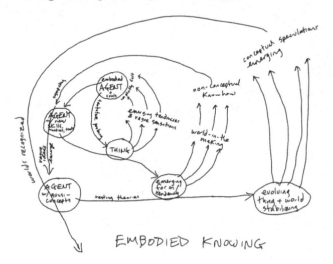

A vague idea about the thing/action (what is it?) emerges and flows back into the making-using-developing process. Quasi-concepts become useful & are tested, stabilized & reactivated. Nascent "theories" are proposed & put to work/tested.

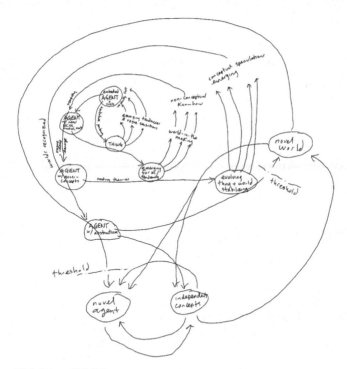

Thinking-Thinking: *thinking about thinking after making:*

Abstraction of concepts from objects/practices. These abstractions feedback (know-how) and feedforward (theories, paradigms, approaches, modes of being) into new iterations of the process. Abstraction.

For our purposes what matters here can be summed up thus: *creativity is not a "thing" that some, or all of us, possess — it is a worldly ecological practice in which any of us can participate.*

Thus creativity, like any other phenomenon that we might imagine happening in the mind/brain, is a dynamic, multi-centered, embedded worldly phenomenon/activity. For too long we have divorced thinking from making, but to avoid the Innovation Paradox and allow for novel innovations to arise we need to realize that making is thinking, and doing precedes conceptualization, and this all happens in a robust highly networked environment.

97

Creativity is an aberrant beauty

What makes a novel world hold together and become visible to us despite its newness?

This is a challenging question: if a novel world is qualitatively different and the criteria, logics, process, and values of the previous world do not hold — how will we ever recognize a new world as it first begins to tentatively emerge? Newness, as we know from our previous discussion of tacit knowledge, is first *felt* prior to being fully conceptualized.

Broad, pervasive and overall sensations (moods or feelings) are part of all experience. In everyday life, while doing mundane tasks, we are accompanied by a pervasive sense of contentment, peace, ease, recognition, and perhaps a little boredom (frustration). And equally, when we move away from the known into difference and novelty distinct qualitative sensations arise and can cue us into the fact that we are onto something different and perhaps important: As our experiments lead us into more chaotic and uncharted territories we feel either "nothing" (this is that feeling of frustration/boredom that sometimes accompanies things that are different: when we experience the odd, but we are impatient because they are not what we recognize, expect or instinctively want) or a form of perplexity. This feeling of perplexity can either be discomforting and subtly push us back into the known, or this perplexity and discomfort can come to feel like a force that propels us further into following an experiment. Then as an experiment evolves towards a nascent world where we are accompanied by a sensation of something like wonder or wonder-horror (wow, but where is this taking us?), or even wonder-disgust (wow, but I would never do that). Then as a novel world fully co-emerges with us, it evokes in us a sense of beauty. Now it will not be a beauty we recognize or feel comfortable with — it will be a feeling of an *aberrant beauty* a — novel and altogether strange, but nonetheless compelling, beauty — a disconcerting beauty.

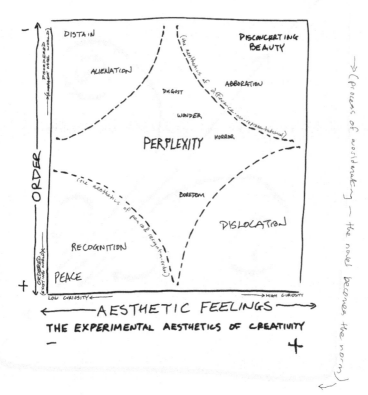

THE EXPERIMENTAL AESTHETICS OF CREATIVITY

Beauty in general is how we sense a world *as a world* — that it is something bigger than we can see, sense, or know *and that it holds together* — we feel it as a beautiful world. Sensing, and welcoming, disconcerting forms of beauty is a critically important skill — it cues us into the opening up of newness in its nascent state. Additionally welcoming these feelings of perplexity, bewilderment, horror, disgust, boredom and wonder open us to an encounter with difference (a new piece of music, a strange cultural artifact, or experiencing a new activity). These feelings are aesthetic feelings -- sensations of beauty. The sensations of beauty and the aesthetic dimensions of experience (and their cultivation) are critical to creativity and invention.

A new form of beauty is integral to a new world — for

a novel world gives us new ways to sense, feel, do, see, and think — which is aesthetics. This feeling and new modes of sensing of wonder and beauty become slowly conceptualizable and enter into discourse and debate and thus transforms into new values, and truths. *Beauty precedes and exceeds truth* as novelty emerges. What is the making of beauty? It is a composition of non-conceptual feelings entangling with the unintended in a strange relay towards a difference that makes a difference. But will this be the beauty we know? No. The new is an aberrant strange and acquired beauty. It beckons us further, it pulls us out and draws us in -- we sense something other and we follow...

PART THREE: STARTING & STAYING IN THE MIDDLE:

With this broad understanding of innovation, emergence, and how to move beyond the innovation paradox, we can now fill in some of the critical contexts for innovation.

ON SYSTEMS, EVENTS, THINGS, AND WORLDS

Life is lived in the middle. The crow finds itself in the midst of an already ongoing situation. It experiments from what it is thrown into. It can never start at some imaginary pure beginning.

The creative life is lived as an interwoven series of ongoing and ultimately unknowable events.

What matters is staying with the middle. Staying with the entangled ongoing relational whole.

When we stop to think about the what and why of things unconsciously we fall into the scripts of our deep cultural habit of pulling everything apart in search of essences.

But where does this desire to get to hidden essences and fundamental building blocks get us?

You can't find anything in anything!

Here's a simple exercise to illustrate the problem: Looking at a bird in flight, where will you find "flight"?

If you pull apart the bird's wings feather by feather will you discover "flight" somewhere inside of something? Is it "in" the feathers? The bones? The Muscles? The shape of the wing?

No, of course not.

Flight is not "in" anything.

Flying is the emergent property of a dynamic system that includes — but is irreducible to — feathers, muscles, gravity, air density, the sun, landscape forms, bones, intentions, practices, ecosystems, evolutionary histories, etc.

Flight happens in the middle.

Creativity dwells in the great outdoors

This analogy holds true with creativity: creativity cannot be found "in" any one thing but is the property *of* a system. Creativity also happens in the middle.

It is not in a brain. It is not in a person. It is not in an idea.

Creativity is the emergent property of a *dynamic system* that includes — *but is irreducible to* —bodies, intentions, practices, habits, cultures, ecosystems, material contexts, evolutionary histories, etc.

What matters here is not any one component of the system, but the system itself. It is less about the unique things and more about *how* they relate — their *relationships*. This shift in focus to a systems level is a shift to working at the level that creativity emerges and lives.

Again, not what it is, but what it affords as an integral part of a set of dynamic relations.

It is the whole that produces the properties we so often mistakenly assign to a part of the system. Flight to feathers, creativity to minds. Behavior to genes.

The properties of the whole need to be understood at the level of the whole.

"Events," "Middles" "Assemblages" and "systems" are simply other ways to talk about this contingent dynamic whole.

Creativity happens at a systems level

Our practices and habits of inquiry in the contemporary West are to think about reality first and foremost in terms of discreet things. We live in a world of chairs, tables, persons, flowers, birds, mountains, rivers, iPhones...

We have the conceptual habit of breaking things down into component parts and building things back up. Societies are composed of groups, groups are composed of families, families are composed of people, people are composed of cells, cells are composed of molecules, molecules are composed of atoms, and on and on all the way down until we come to a string in eleven dimensional space.

We are always peeling away the layers to get at the final inner ingredient which we then understand as singular and solitary essence. The onion model.

ESSENCE
• DEEP
• TRUE
• CORE
• UNCHANGE
• IMMATERIAL

SURFACE
• SUPERFICIAL
• CHANGING
• IMPOSED
• MATERIAL

ONION MODEL

This is connected to its companion habit of neatly dividing everything into two — essential and superficial. A gesture repeated in all our dualities: with always one term superseding the other as more essential: nature and culture, mind and body, men and women, right and left... But what if the "essence" or logic, or driving force is not in any one thing but held across the whole relationship? What if it is relations all the way down and all the way up?

Perhaps the easiest and first way to understand relations is the connection between things. Love, for example, is not in anything but held between and across people, places, things and activities. Love, creativity, flight, an event or an idea — all of these are things that come from the totality of a set of relations. These "connections" — such as creativity are as real as the things themselves.

Our world is composed of many forms of relationships: feelings, actions, practices, bodies, environments, brains, energy gradients, laws, predator-prey pairings, concepts, feedback loops, mindsets, and worldviews, are all examples of relationships.

But so too are things -- our hammer, when we grasp and use it is clearly a hard and solid *thing* to us but it is also very much a relational being. A hammer is impossible to imagine without something to hammer. A hammer calls to metals forged into nails and trees sawn into boards and a world where they make sense. This world — this system is one quite distinct from one of vines and woven branches, or mud bricks.

When we see things and all their relationships as connected, we begin to see worlds and systems. But seeing connections is only the beginning. A system is fundamentally more than a set of connected things.

Systems are Weird

When we connect things, the parts are superseded by the totality and *this totality takes on a logic all of its own* — one that is irreducible to the parts and their initial logics. (Which is why you cannot take systems apart to find out how they work).

Here we are introducing a second concept to the reality of relations — the unique reality of the whole. What is most shocking about systems is that when you put things into a set of relationships something totally new and unexpected will *emerge* (this novelty is what is termed emergence and we will discuss this shortly).

Systems act in unique ways that cannot be understood or *changed* by looking at individual things — in fact considering the parts individually will usually make things worse. This is where understanding systems really matters to creativity and innovation.

Let's dig into a great example: Single-use plastic bags are a serious problem. Many innovators have approached this problem from the perspective that this is an issue that can be addressed by dealing with the plastic bag alone (versus from a systems perspective). This perspective has led to the very popular move to ban plastic bags as a solution. On the surface, it does seem like an ideal solution to curbing the use of plastics and limiting all of the problems that come from these bags and plastic in general. It is a very popular and easy to grasp action: ban bags!

But what actually happens when you ban plastic bags? Does the use of plastics go down? Is the overall harm to the environment reduced? No — the opposite actually happens: the use of plastics and other harmful practices actually goes up. That this might be a surprise, and this surprise is a testament to how poorly we understand systems.

Here is what happens when you ban plastic bags in supermarkets:

1. The first thing to understand is that people use shopping bags for all sorts of things: trash can liners, dog poop bags, general storage, etc. So if they do not get these for free while shopping they have to buy bags and when you buy bags you buy for quality — thus not only are you buying the equivalent number of bags — you are buying thicker bags. Thus more plastic and more plastic bags.

2. Stores that cannot offer plastic bags still have to offer consumers alternative options: paper bags (the product of forests being turned into tree farms plus lots of chemicals), or cloth reusable bags. These cloth bags are made from cotton — our biggest crop and also our most toxic crop. And reusable heavy duty plastic bags — well, even more plastic. So now we have added at least three increased streams of problematic manufacturing.

3. Not only haven't you cut down on pollution, you have used up huge amounts of the community's collective energy to get make change happen, but you have only made things worse. Which in itself leads to a cycle of resignation and or the renewed hunt for the "real" culprit.

But there is no "real" culprit — *it is a systems problem.* Systems are surprising and almost always work counter to our intuition. To innovate, to invent, and to be creative — which is to say to make some kind of difference in the world, no matter the scale, we need to take into account how systems (and not discreet things) behave.

Creativity happens across assemblages

Things do not appear alone — they are always part of a system — connected to other things, practices, habits, environments and purposes — which is to say that ultimately things cohere, emerge from, and circle back into a coherent ecosystem *or world.* When we work on anything we both work as and on an assemblage: we are using tools, practices, concepts, specific environments, habits, modes of organizing, etc. It is critical to recognize that to innovate at the level of a change in kind you have to develop a novel "task-space" — a specific system, environment and assemblage that will let you have an impact.

Probing, testing, following hunches, purturbating systems and following exaptive affordances is not a one-off activity, it needs to be connected to an ecosystem organized towards its "success." This is the development of the right environment, assemblage, and task-space.

It is important to remember that in all assemblages there are clear and explicit parts and a vast sea of tacit and implicit parts, practices, and activities — don't ignore the tacit.

Creativity is worldmaking

To radically innovate at a systems level— to make a change in kind emerge is to co-evolve with a novel world. With any radical change-in-kind there co-emerges an ontologically new world.

Critical to all disruptive change is the practice and process of worldmaking.

Here we can return to our initial framing of change as a double loop of change-in-degree giving rise to change-in-kind and vice versa. In addition to understanding the differences between developmental and disruptive change, we have to consider the unique aspects *within* each.

Disruptive forms of change are categorically different from developmental change. While we experience and participate in developmental changes continuously, we have far less experience with disruptive change. And it is quite common to consider disruptive change simply a bigger, stronger and more radical version of developmental change. So often disruptive change is imaged as an extreme form of creativity where one simply breaks all the rules or just does crazy things — but disruptive change has a clear logic and process that can be understood and followed.

To properly understand disruptive change we have to understand that it is a qualitative change. A qualitative change can be best understood as a *change in worlds.* The shift from horse transportation to automobiles is a good example: cars did not simply replace horses as the common means of transportation. Cars and all that they entail (resource extraction, roads, motors, mass transportation, mental models, new industries, huge corporations, new nation-states, habits, etc.), gave us a new world far different from the world of relying on and living with other creatures. These two worlds (horse world vs car world) while having some outward similarities are categorically (qualitatively) different. With this insight into changes in worlds we can properly define disruptive innovation as an act of worldmaking. There are many examples of worldmaking innovations: writing, the wheel, domesticating plants and animals, God and Gods, evolutionary theory, capitalism, electricity, the internal combustion engine, contraceptives, the evolution of life, Polynesian navigation techniques — the list is long...

What counts as a disruptive change? The answer is both simple and ambiguous: anything could end up becoming a qualitative change — but we would only know in retrospect, based upon its level of qualitative change. (Disruptive innovations produce novel worlds which, by definition, cannot be known in advance).

All disruptive innovations are a rolling of the dice — we cannot know what they will become, do or mean in advance — all we can do is participate in their making. (This is an emergent process that Evan Thompson refers to as "laying down the path in walking.")

At the heart of the Innovation Design Approach is this process of qualitative change and worldmaking — which we can now add to our basic double-loop diagram:

Now that we have a sense of the two forms of change and the role of worldmaking, we can ask the question: *how does one get to the point of making a new world?* The first part of the answer is that you have to disclose and understand the underlying logic of the world that you are currently in — for without a critical understanding of the current world it is most likely that our creative actions will simply continue to reproduce this world.

Hence, prior to actually innovating, a critical practice is Disclosure. Disclosure is no easy task as the worlds that we inhabit are almost totally invisible to us — we simply take them to be "reality". And if anything outside or different from our world should appear to us it appears most often as something illogical, absurd, plain wrong, even totally impossible, or simply invisible. Difficulties aside, we can now see that there are at least three distinct phases to innovation:

1.   Disclose (understand the world you are in)

2. Deviate (to make a novel world possible), and..

3. Emerge (make that world real).

Then, based upon our first four points about the need for deep engagement, we can add an initial phase: Engage. From this we have developed a basic process diagram that we will use throughout the book:

The Innovation Design Approach is about making a new world possible. Creativity and innovation are always about something bigger than finding and solving an existing problem. Creativity is worldmaking and in doing so old problems are less solved than rendered moot.

in the beginning was the event

PART FOUR: FINAL CONCEPTS (SUMMING IT UP & GETTING GOING)

SEVEN CONCEPTS TO REMEMBER AS ONE BEGINS:

1. Creativity is a learned skill

So often one hears: "we are all born creative", "creativity cannot be taught, some people are just born more creative", "school beats the creativity out of us". While this sounds great, and we can all relate to these claims — after all who does not feel creative, or that some others seem far more creative? And most certainly most of us have very mixed feelings about school. But is this really the case?

I think that we should be able to see at this point in our discussion of creativity why this argument is wrong. This argument rests on a series of false assumptions:

1. Creativity is a uniquely human phenomenon

2. Creativity is a purely mental (brain-based) phenomenon

3. Brains come wired a certain way and the wiring can be improved to some degree, but ultimately you are a certain way because of your neurology, and...

4. Nature vs Nurture (born that way vs learned to be that way)

Are all valid ways to frame the human nature and learning debate. While it should be obvious, based upon the previous sections that these assumptions are wrong, what matters more is that *they are beside the point:* creativity is a worldly practice and as such — like all other worldly practices, we can learn to join it and further: learn practices that support its likelihood of happening and continuing. And it follows that creativity is learned.

This should be great news: practices to foster novel outcomes can be learned. To be creative is to participate constructively in worldly creativity. This requires many skills from the conceptual to the physical. More important than debating endlessly Nature vs Nurture it is best to get on with the important contemporary task of innovating. This is what the Innovation Design Approach strives to develop: To think differently, we first have to act and live differently — and this will always be a collective and more-than-human project.

The Innovation Design Approach also recognizes that the above model of embodied doing leading to embodied knowing is, by itself, *not sufficient for developing creative outcomes*. Doing something different requires concrete practices that block and experiment beyond the explicit and implicit logic of the given. And doing this requires learning, and just as importantly *unlearning*, many habits, practices, concepts, histories, etc.

2. Creativity is negative to become a positive

The historical image of creativity and invention is a state of being free — free of all the limits, constraints, rules put on us. Freedom and creativity are seen as synonymous — creativity is the state in which you are finally liberated from everything that holds you back and able to do precisely what one wants.

This model of creativity is based on a false opposition between order and freedom. But we know from our previous sections that creativity involves the double act of (1) knowing what is going on (disclosing), and (2) then *not* doing this (deviating).

This second phase can be confused with a "just be free" approach. But it is all about rules — negative rules: you need to *stop doing* what has been done before — and this means developing rules to *block* you from repeating the past. These rules are constraints that are generative. If we put in place a rule to block using brushes to paint we open up the field of painting to radical new possibilities. And the better, more carefully, and more thorough we develop these blockages, the more radical and novel the outcome will be. A creative process is only as good as what it refuses.

Creativity and innovation do not involve getting rid of all constraints once and for all, rather they need constraints. Rules are paradoxically liberating. The beginning of the move from disclosing to deviating is blocking. The process of blocking involves inventing and collaborating with new generative constraints in such a way as to lead to novel outcomes. Rules matter, the issue is how to make them.

3. Creativity is problem producing

Rather than defining creativity as a "freedom from" (the freedom from all limits) or the outcome of a perfect idea (the liberty + brilliance model of creativity) we define creativity "problematically" and focus on the generative process of transformation, which is driven by constraints and the questions or problems they generate. The creative process is driven by problems and the fields of possibilities they generate.

Creativity is the outcome of a set of practices that lead us to invent and pose new and profound world making problems. To make sense of this we need to take a brief detour into the world of problems and questions.

What is a problem? In a very simple sense, we could say that it is the stating of a question. The structure of a question or problem contains within it the possibility of an answer or solution. The question necessarily precedes the answer — if you cannot articulate the question then no answer can be generated. Solutions are always connected to the question that generated them. Thus being able to create a problem is a generative act, and one that already encompasses the possibility of the answers that might eventually emerge.

Henri Bergson frames the role of problems in creativity

this way, "It is a question of finding the problem... even more than of solving it. For a speculative problem is solved as soon as it is properly stated".

This is quite a radical statement — think of our K-12 education system with its focus on giving students questions to solve and solely focusing on the quality of the answers. Bergson flips this model on its head: what matters is the generation of a question because in the question "a solution already exists then, although it may remain hidden and, so to speak, covered up: the only thing left to do is uncover it".

Problems already contain, in a hidden manner, their solution. How can this be? The first part of the answer is quite general: If we pose a problem, say "how can we support the human body in repose?" we will have generated an immanent space in which every mode of sitting, lying, leaning will eventually emerge and find a place. But this is far too vague to be of much use — we could be waiting a very long time for anything to come of such a general question. Bergson offers us an important clue "a speculative problem is solved as soon as it is properly stated."

What is a properly stated question? Questions/problems come to us embedded in a network of unspoken assumptions, approaches and practices that frame and support the way the question/problem is posed. As we bring these into the light we see the actual contours of the problem. The more we dig into these assumptions (the "world" that we discussed above), the more we can see how critical it is to both uncover our assumptions and frame the problem/question in the best manner possible. Thus a properly stated question would articulate what is hidden — and block the assumptions that limit the new from emerging.

Solutions to problems are what we would call inventions. An example: a chair is one solution or invention to the problem (question), "How can we support the human body in repose?" The chair is a (now) very standard solution to the question. A chair accepts a problem as it is currently framed by our conventions and habits. This mode of taking a problem as given (with all of its hidden assumptions in place) leads to a "change-in-degree" solution (e.g. perhaps our chair is a "better" chair with some unique feature). But, Bergson is not simply interested in elucidating the structure of existing problems — quite the opposite, for Bergson the most important aspect of problems is that they are not fixed. Problems must be made, " stating the problem is not simply uncovering, it is *inventing*.

Discovery, or uncovering has to do with what already exists; it was, therefore, certain to happen sooner or later. Invention gives being to what did not exist; it might never have happened... The effort of invention consists of most often by raising the problem, in creating the terms it is stated". In inventing and radically reframing a problem we move from the world of "it will happen sooner or later" to one of true novelty (change-in-kind). Perhaps the biggest mistake in innovation is that far too often we assume problems as they are stated. All radical innovation involves inventing the problem — either through a radical reframing, or through the development of a totally new question.

Creativity is problematic. We are inventing new problems to develop new worlds that can lead to novel outcomes. If it were only that easy! This is not the end of the story, "the truly great problems are set forth only when they are solved." We cannot ignore the previous key arguments about creativity, and simply replace brainstorming answers with questions! When we are trying to be radically inventive, we can know what we do not want, but since the new does not yet exist *it resists all formalization* — even into a problem statement. Thus when pursuing a disruptive path of innovation we might know what not to do (or what to block), but we need to experimentally allow the problem to co-emerge with our experiments. The goal then of blocking and experimenting is not to produce a solution or even an alternative world — that only comes much, much later — first we need to generate a portal, an opening, an experimental path — and this is where the blocking of old assumptions and the generating of novel quasi-questions will help us in deviating. Later we will come to understand what our actual novel question is...

4. Creativity is not neutral

Creativity has a history. Why in this moment of increasingly precarious forms of work, and the ever-widening disparity between the ultra-wealthy and everyone else are we all being encouraged to be more flexible, creative and innovative?

In whose service are these ideas and values?

Creativity and innovation are inherently loaded issues. We need to think critically about our contemporary reality. Are we being creative just to make new trendy widgets? Or are new worlds possible? What are we trying to sustain? What is really needed?

The Innovation Design Approach sees that the creativity, invention, and innovation that we champion are not neutral goods. We live in a very dangerous moment which requires both caution and innocence. Everything, as Foucault said, is dangerous, and new worlds are possible. But, this does not mean we champion creativity and the new above all else, we need a critical visionary creativity that understands that we are not separate from all the consequences of what emerges from what we initiate.

5. Creativity never begins from zero

Get out of your head, get out of your studio, get out of your ideas, get out of your brainstorming session and join the world — engage, probe, experiment.

You do not need a clean slate — and this will never be possible — embrace the complexity of things, work with others, surrender to the process: co-emerge and co-evolve from this world here and now.

We promise — interesting, surprising and worthwhile things will happen — they just won't be what any of us expected — but, hey — that is a really really good thing!

6. Creativity has no Method

As you read this it would be very easy to mist. Innovation Design Approach for a capital M "Methou. Innovation Design is not a Method, but a set of pragmatic tools and procedures. Why bring this up? There is an easy dogmatism and false sense of security in Methods, which in their one-size-fits-all exuberance can all-too-readily squash curiosity, difference, possibilities and ultimately innovation. Whitehead, says it well, "Some of the major disasters of mankind have been produced by the narrowness of men with a good methodology."

Today, Methods of innovation abound. Design Thinking and the Lean Canvas are just two of the most popular Methods being taught on a global scale such that their limits and problems as Methods have become obvious. Despite this, or perhaps because of it, they remain an entrenched dogmatic force in the world of innovation.

The Innovation Design Approach, as a set of skills, should not be mistaken for a one-size-fits-all Method. We are trying the best we can to avoid the limits and blind spots of Methods -- whether historical models or more recent user-centered models such as Design Thinking, by offering an open and flexible set of practices combined with a philosophical outlook. What looks like a Method in this document is an attempt to do two distinct, and possibly contradictory things, (1) develop new creative processes/tools for innovation and (2) find a way to teach these in a simple manner. (If you wish to insist upon calling it a method then it is only in the sense that Herman Melville claims for himself, "There are some enterprises in which a careful disorderliness is the true method.")

Our aversion to Methods should not be mistaken for a willingness to offer a laissez-faire approach. Innovation Design has a distinct style of creativity Innovation Design puts experimental worldmaking at the core of innovation in contrast to most western models of innovation and design that have focused on generating ideas, and solutions.

We believe that innovation, at its most creative, is a worldmaking and not an idea or product making practice. Innovations are assemblages of novel deeply embodied practices, tools, implicit mentalities, concepts, environments and goals. It is this assemblage that what we are calling a "world." Experimental worldmaking is a fundamentally engaged, responsive and emergent practice that re-orients creativity towards an embedded, co-evolving, problem producing, worldmaking and systems based practice. In short it is a hands-on worldly and experimental action-oriented collaborative approach.

If creativity is not pre-existing in the head then it depends wholly on practice — why some people are more "creative" is simply because they have practiced and fully embodied techniques of the innovation process. This goes for organizations, collectives and events — practice matters.

This philosophical critique and alternative focus is not about winning an intellectual debate about the definition of creativity, it matters deeply because our most pressing issues today from climate change to equality are complex, dynamic, systemic and open-ended problems that cannot be effectively addressed (and have often been caused or exacerbated) by narrow, linear solution centric methods of design and innovation.

Let's invent problems worth having for worlds worth making!

7. Creativity *requires us to fundamentally rethink who we are*

Enough said — this should be obvious by now — and hopefully you are already changed and rethinking some fundamental things...

engage

disclose

deviate

emerge

HOW TO INNOVATE: THE TASKS AND PRACTICES
THE FOUR TASKS OF INNOVATION DESIGN

Over the years, as we researched and developed our understanding of innovation, it has always been directly tied to the practical activity of actually innovating.

Working on projects from wetland remediation to developing new learning models have been our testing grounds. With each project came a new experiment in evolving a better innovation process.

While we realized early on that the classical three step process of ideate, plan and make (and all of its countless variations) would never lead to innovation, it took us much longer to develop a powerful alternative holistic process.

1. IDEATE   2. PLAN   3. MAKE

Working on many highly diverse projects has forced us to develop many discreet tools and practices that answered specific innovation roadblocks.

How to:

- do real experiments for novelty

- disclose and block the known

- engage and follow the unintended

- develop alternative worlds

- be far more embodied and rely on know-how over know-what

These tools were enormously helpful. But innovation is not simply about deploying a set of powerful tools in an ad hoc method — it is about the sequencing of a coherent process.

As our understanding evolved, so too did our process. We have been articulating, testing, and remaking this process through countless iterations. Even when we thought we had it all perfectly worked out — to the point we designed and had a series of posters printed — the surprising nature of innovation itself forced us back to the lab to continue honing the process. (We still have the stack of posters to remind us of our own hubris).

For the last five years we've continued refining our process of innovation that consists of four tasks:

1. Engage
2. Disclose
3. Deviate
4. Emerge

These four tasks can be thought of as a set of interconnected practices or activities. Each takes on a distinct aspect of the innovation process:

- **Engage** and **Disclose** are the tasks necessary to prepare for innovation,

- **Deviate** and **Emerge** are the two distinct processes that foster the two distinct forms of change:

    - change-in-degree (Emerge), and

    - change-in-kind (Deviate).

- While **Deviate** fosters a disruptive change, which comes early in the process,

- **Emerge** as a developmental process, always comes at the end to make things real.

Hence the sequential order of (1) Engage, (2) Disclose, (3) Deviate, (4) Emerge.

128

Even though these are interconnected tasks where one flows to the next, diagramming this, or any innovation process, as circular is, as we realized when we had those posters printed, a huge mistake.

With a circle we immediately lose sight of the fact that there are two radically distinct processes at the heart of innovation:

1.   change-in-degree (developmental change), and

2.   change-in-kind (disruptive change)

... each of which requires a wholly distinct process. And each moving in a wholly different direction.

Remembering this, made us realize that innovation is not circular — it is composed of two connected loops going in opposite directions.

The loop of Deviation points *backward* and the loop of Emerge points *forward*.

Developing or improving something degree by degree is a progressive and forward moving process. And disruption and the development of a whole new approach is to rupture this forward movement of progress. This needs to be shown and understood as two distinct but connected loops:

Understanding the two distinct pathways of innovation still leaves the key question unanswered: *How to begin?*

All activity of change begins by leaving your office, leaving your studio — getting out of your head and joining with the world in a fully engaged manner.

In this way we don't start by ideating, empathizing or innovating, we start by immersing ourselves deeply in an ongoing reality. Therefore, the **Engage** phase begins the process.

From engagement we find ourselves at a true crossroads — we have to decide:

- are we interested in developing within the context of what already exists?

- or do we wish to be more radical and develop something that is truly novel?

Thus we show engage as moving both:

- *forward* to continue into a developmental innovation process (**Emerge**):

- *stepping backwards* from the forward rush of progress to pause and understand the deep hidden logic of your current reality (**Disclose**) and enter into a process of **Deviation** from that reality:

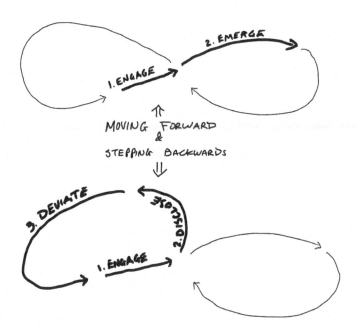

While **Engagement, Deviation** and **Emergence** are simplest to understand and often get all the attention — it is **Disclosure** that is key to everything in innovation. No matter what you do — you will never develop a deep and disruptive paradigm busting worldmaking innovation if you do not uncover and block a series of existing practices, habits and worlds.

With a basic understanding of these four phases and how they connect to the two loops of change we can lay out a simple diagram of the full process:

GETTING MORE DETAILED:
THE 15 PRACTICES OF INNOVATION

THE 15 PRACTICES
OF
INNOVATION

Once oriented to the big picture we can now move into the detailed process of innovation. While we can think of the innovation process as one where we move through four general tasks, what we are really doing is a series of sequential practices. Innovation is ultimately a journey — a strange and surprising journey of twists and turns, many dead-ends, strange leaps, shocks, moments of great beauty and wonderment, a lot of mundane work, and what might seem like endless repetition — all with the goal of making something emerge that is wholly unexpected.

There are fifteen distinct practices, roughly 3-5 in each task. Each practice consists of a number of distinct research programs, experiments and questions. In the next section of the book we will lay out in detail how to engage with each task and their related practices, but for now an overview will help introduce the actual work of innovation.

The Engage task is both the initial steps in the process of innovation and the beginning of a practice of deep engagement that continues throughout all of the phases of innovation.

In a certain sense the engage phase is about learning how to leave the secure and known and join the flow of life. It is about getting out of your head and getting out of your comfort zone and engaging. Not much in life, never mind innovation, will happen without doing this.

Often there is a strong temptation to skip this step, we assume we already know all the answers and can move on to the real work of innovating. But the full immersion into a world and a question with others builds a shared ecosystem — a commons that becomes the expansive well that novelty can, in all its surprising glory, emerge.

We divide this task up into three practices, which while presented as being sequential, are ultimately deeply interwoven:

1. Opening & Grounding: Why and where one begins an innovation journey is truly diverse. Sometimes it is an idea, at other times a vexing question, or perhaps an observation, or a persistent problem. You can begin anywhere. When you begin matters little, it is how you go that counts. This task begins that process by both opening you up to the larger space of the question and grounding you in the lived world of that question.

2. Attuning & Gathering: As you ground yourself in a question it is important to connect with others — to participate and engage in the world surrounding your area of interest. Develop a collaborative community. What do they do? What is their history? What are their concerns? How can you make a shared space of curiosity?

3. Pattern Recognition: As one dwells in the larger world of a question and connects with a community equally entangled in this question the collective activity of uncovering the underlying logics, habits, histories and trends can begin.

Disclosure is a continuation of the Pattern Recognition activity that ended the Engage task. But in this new task of Disclosure the critical activity of uncovering is only half of what we seek to discover.

What is unique about the Disclosure is that it splits into two distinct parallel paths. One path focuses on a critical uncovering of the implicit logic of current practices, and the other path focuses on discovering and exploring unintentional possibilities. It is these two wholly distinct parallel activities that will allow for disruptive innovation to emerge in the next task: Deviation.

4. Defining: By critically interrogating the scope, history, and implicit logic of one's question during the task of Engage, one is now prepared to define the larger "matter of concern" in regards to which your question is simply one historically contingent approach. Grasping that you're concerned with something bigger than a question or framework allows you to release yourself from your narrow focus on the question, problems and solutions— and ultimately open yourself up to the possibility that there is a whole other way of being alive that might not even contain this question, issue or problem. This activity could be equally well named as "releasement".

5. Uncovering: Innovation cannot begin to get novel if it stops at uncovering a history or discovering trends, it needs to go deeper. What is the framework, paradigm or even world that gives rise to a way of being alive that evolves these issues, questions, problems and practices? It is only when this question is answered at an *ontological level* that one can begin to innovate in a profound manner.

We do this because we know that other worlds are possible and the goal of innovation is the realization of another world.

6. Exploration (towards the unintended): Parallel to uncovering the underlying logics of your issue/question you need to discover unintended possibilities within the objects, environments, habits and frameworks entangled with your broad area of interest (which you discovered and joined in during the Emerge task). These unintended possibilities are what will drive your disruptive innovation experiments in the next task of innovation: Deviate.

DEVIATE

The task of Deviation is to deliberately put the known path aside and co-emerge a novel and new path via considered experimentation.

The goal of Deviation is not to come up with a solution or a product — that comes much later in the process. The goal of Deviation is to develop a new and novel approach to your matter of concern.

This "approach" can range in scope from a radical but small scale innovation to something paradigm busting and truly worldmaking.

Here, during the task of Deviation, the ontological new emerges via a process of exaptive design. While the multiple practices of Engage and Disclose are holistic and do overlap, with Deviate that is not the case, it is important to do these sequentially.

7. Staging: *This involves two things: (1)*

1. defining the scope and scale of what can change, and

2. deciding what to block and what to follow.

It is here that one sets up what Erin Manning calls the "enabling constraint" — that which you refuse.
This comes out of the activity of Uncovering.

Ideally one blocks or refuses a paradigm or world. Such a blocking will potentially lead to the greatest possible novelty.

As critical as what is blocked is the question of what is followed. This grows out of the activity of Exploration where promising unintended possibilities have been discovered. Once the initial conditions blocking and following are staged it is time to move onto the activity of Experimentation.

8. Experimenting: With what is blocked and what will be followed in place one carries out a series of experiments, following, stabilizing and co-emerging unintended possibilities.

These experiments follow what we term the Exaptive Innovation Process. This involves a series of iterative experiments in blocking and following that move one ever further into the unknown — the new and novel.

9. Transversal Articulation: As the practice of experimentation progresses one needs to take stock from the perspective of the emergent novelty that is being developed.

As humans we are deeply connected to our past and the reasons for what we do and did. This practice allows us to step out of that history and past and see the new for what it is and what it could be. We are pausing to articulate our transversal (sideways) moves in their full radicality so we can continue to experiment, but from the perspective of what is being born.

10. Worlding: The preceding practices lead one into an emerging novel paradigm/world. Worlds are not discovered but co-emerged and co-evolved.

Now it is time to pause the experiments and attempt to collectively articulate what new approach and what new world is beginning to emerge. This practice is both speculative and ontological. The crux is to keep the emergent difference alive and not reduce the possible to the merely probable. The articulation of worlding is also the articulation of tools, practices, embodiments and territories (it is not an idea). A novel assemblage is forming.

Worlding: one can think of the entire process of innovation as this task.

The danger is to see this activity as "ideation" where a vision of the future is made and that everything from this point forward is just planning and executing on this vision. That would be to fall back into the "God model" of innovation.

The activity of worlding does not magically produce a world but builds out an emergent path into a possible territory that will later take on a life of its own.

[Ouroboros: Quite often the activity of worlding falls back into the known. This is to be expected. Radical innovation is difficult. The activity of Ouroboros is to assist in pushing your emergent novelty further via a series of paradoxical techniques where the world turns upon itself and emerges as another.]

11. Strategic Joining: Other worlds are possible and yes other worlds can be speculatively developed. But, how does this have a meaningful transformative impact on our reality? Strategic Joining seeks to begin to test answers and possible pathways to transformational impact.

EMERGE

The task of emergence is to make the radical possibilities drawn forth into a nascent state of existence during Deviation real, concrete and impactful. This is a highly strategic and experimental phase where the goal is no longer to deviate but to make the deviations transform our current reality.

This happens by probing and testing and co-evolving both a community and a "product". This "product" — whatever it might be — a thing, a service, an event — is ultimately an ecosystem. And it is the ecosystem's emergence and ever evolving state of thriving that is the "goal" of Emerge. The practices of Emerge are sequential and highly iterative — to make anything emerge and become transformative is to test, shift and repeat; many, many times.

12. Emergent Transition: Emergence begins by transitioning from a world of qualitative change to the world of developmental change. Slowly a concrete ecosystem needs to be developed.

During the activity of transition one probes and tests critical points in existing systems to see how it responds. These unique and unpredictable responses guide the process as they reveal emergent pathways and leverage points in the system. In the activity of probing a new collective — a new community and culture begins to configure around the activity.

13. Coevolution: Things are starting to cohere in surprising ways: new practices are emerging alongside a budding community and culture. It is this nascent ecosystem that one needs to co-evolve into an ever more stable and fully realized state.

There is a relay that emerges between people, practices,

tools, ideas, and values that is leading towards the founding of new ways of doing and being. Much of this will be a surprise. The practices of coevolution need to embrace these surprises and transform along with them.

14. Ecosystem Building: Novel worlds are not ideas — they are coherent and stable assemblages of interconnected networks of tools, practices, resources, values, and communities.

Great care and attention has to be given to supporting and stabilizing this as it emerges in a "spontaneous" manner. Ecosystem building is this practice and in a very real sense the practices of Coevolution and Ecosystem Building never end — things persist because we make it possible.

15. Amplification: The effectiveness of any system relies on many amplifying and reinforcing feedback loops. These need to loop into new territories and possibilities as well as loop-back deeper into the process. Ideally one is looping back into the Disruptive task to renew the novel potentials of your ecosystem.

[Feedback: When nearing the end of a task it is critical to set up a more formal check-in or feedback session. This should be designed in a manner that is specific to the context.]

HOW TO HACK THE INNOVATION DESIGN PROCESS

While we just wrote out the process of innovation as an almost linear singular step by step process — there is no one proper way through the loops of innovation.

Innovation has no fixed starting point. Innovation has no fixed path. And ultimately innovation has no proper endpoint.

Where you start and how you proceed is entirely dependent on where you are and where you are trying to go.

Equally where you start and where you end up can be determined by many outside forces.

While we recommend, for the sake of learning the total process of innovation, that you follow this workbook from beginning to end, know that the linear step by step process will rarely be the innovation journey you take.

Once you understand the process you can jump to the phase that best suits your needs, and develop a novel pathway.

For the sake of demonstrating the flexibility and possibilities of the process lets look four common pathways through the innovation process:

1. You have a clear understanding of what you wish to develop:

This is the path of most entrepreneurs and designers. When you have a clear idea about what you wish to make you can start with Engage and then move directly to Emerge.

While this path often seems the fastest and most straightforward — don't be fooled: the process is loopy -- you are going backwards – iterating, testing, revising, changing often.

The advantages of this path is its directness, the dangers of this path is that we end up with a one-off product — we never fully develop an ecosystem nor realize the world expanding or world grounding possibilities of what we are making. We call this being "world-blind" and it is the fate of many an inventor.

The answer to the problem of being world-blind is to loop through the disclose phase to see what world your emerging novel concept is a part of.

2. You have an existing product or service to evolve:

Often one already has a product or service in circulation, and the question is how does one enrich a (narrow) innovation (your solution) into a resilient (business) ecosystem or a more robust solution?

Or perhaps you are simply interested in developing what could come next out of what you have already done.

For this you are beginning at the "end" of the Emerge phase and looping back into the world disclosing practices of the Disclose phase. This allows you to experimentally uncover the deeper logics and richer paradigmatic potentials of your concept area. This process of deep paradigmatic uncovering moves one away from a narrow solution towards a resilient and robust ecosystem of multiple opportunities.

With this deep paradigmatic understanding you now move back through the Engage and Emerge tasks where you are testing out these expanded possibilities and forming a community of users. This process will then lead you into the final phase of where you develop these possibilities into a reality.

3. You wish to disrupt an existing approach:

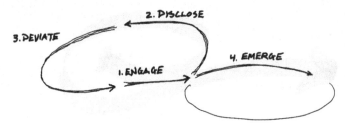

At the core of all innovation and making is the ever present potential for genuine novelty known as Disruptive Innovation.

This is where the Innovation Design Framework offers a powerful new approach: Engage, Disclose, Deviate, Emerge.

While we have already covered this in the previous section it is good to remember the process: Engagement moves backward into the uncovering of existing approaches/paradigms, and unintended possibilities which are then experimentally

Developed via a sideways process of iterative blocking and following to develop a novel world. It is only after a novel world or paradigm has been developed that one can move towards the development of problems and solutions which define classical design and entrepreneurship strategies.

4. Some Stand Alone Tools:

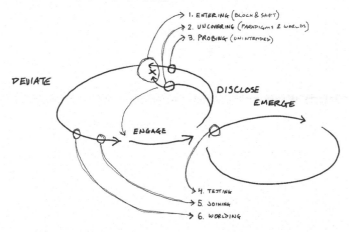

Ultimately all the various components of the innovation process can be used alone or in new non-linear connections with each other. Here are six that we use quite often and why:

1. Uncovering (Approaches, Paradigms and Worlds): Change can only really happen when one knows what is going on at a deep level. We will use these techniques in a fast manner (diagramming forms) throughout. As you get good at seeing patterns you begin to recognize ones that repeat and it becomes easier to put them aside.

2. Exploration (towards *Unintended Potentials):* This activity of using things in novel ways (puttering, playing and improvising) is part of our everyday lives — we are always asking: *what else can this do that was not intended?* Here too, the more one does it the more one recognizes this everywhere in life.

3. Staging and Experimenting (Block & Shift): Again an everyday technique we use constantly: block something and force yourself to act and think differently. The blockage does not need to be big, and can be fun (block utensils at dinner). Not a moment goes by when the thought of blocking something does not arise. Critical at every point of innovation.

4. Worlding: One exercise we do quite a bit is taking new and strange things and then speculating on what novel mode of being alive it suggests — what portal to novel modes of being could they open up?

Far too often we are world-blind and miss how potentially revolutionary simple things can be.

In the story of innovators it is far too often someone else that sees the worldmaking potential for something — inventors are often too close to what they make or are working under the mistaken assumption that their invention simply "solves a problem". It is important to always be aware of the alternative worldmaking potential of all things — especially the most mundane.

5. Strategic Joining (Map & Relocate &/or Re-engage): Mapping and diagramming and other forms of visual thinking are critical at every moment — reality, change and creativity are dynamic nonlinear processes that diagrams help us to visualize best. Mapping shows diverse potentials and multiple alternative pathways, this gets us out of our fixation on single answers and narrow solution paths.

6. Probing: This one step is a way of testing a system to see what might emerge. In complex highly dynamic situations probing becomes the only way to get a sense of what is going on. Probes also keep us honest and outside of "solution thinking".

REVIEW

Innovation Design brings innovation out of the mystical realms and makes it a concrete pragmatic process that can be explicated for the sake of learning in a series of steps.

This is not to claim that one can equate pragmatic with easy or a guarantee of success. One is never done learning the craft of making, and each project we undertake requires us to begin again and creatively re-invent the processes.

INNOVATION DESIGN

1. *Innovation* is production of the genuinely new

2. *Design* is a process of action towards an outcome = Innovation Design is the process for producing the genuinely new.

INNOVATION

1. The *new* is when change happens that produces a difference.

2. There are two types of difference: Difference-in-degree, and Difference-in-kind

3. These two forms of difference/change correspond to two distinct forms of Innovation: Developmental and Disruptive.

4. Developmental Innovation is incremental, world expanding, quantitative, probabilistic, and improving.

5. Disruptive is rupturing, qualitative, possibilistic, and world making.

PROCESSES FOR INNOVATION

There are four key processes that distinguishes Innovation Design:

1. **Engage:** Beginning with a matter of interest or concern actively collectively immerse yourself collectively in its world(s) in a way that evolves deep and sustained fully immersive engagement. The Engage phase requires you to foster collectivity, commons, intra-dependency, belonging and open embedded engagement. Notice patterns, trends, and trajectories as they emerge. You are staging an encounter.

2. **Disclose:** Via deep engagement (phase one) disclose the underlying logic, habits, patterns, paradigms and world of your matter of concern. Uncover multiple qualitatively different modes and pathways. In this activity notice unintended potentialities of matters and practices.

3. **Deviate:** Disruptive Innovation: begin by blocking critical aspects of an existing world, paradigm, and or habits. Then via an iterative open experimental embodied and physically grounded process of deviation evolve a radically new world or paradigm, habits and patterns. Relocate and or reconnect and develop this world in an engaged manner.

4. **Emerge:** Starting from either where you are, or beginning to develop your novel world (emerging from the previous phases), probe and iteratively co-evolve collectively to concretely realize a specific outcome.

AN ETHOS FOR APPROACHING CREATIVITY: PRACTICES FOR INNOVATION

To allow creative processes to flourish in our lives we need to change our general approach to life. Here are some suggestions:

Value:

- ...becoming over being

- ...novelty over permanence

- ...difference over identity

- ...repetition over reflection

- ...long emergence over sudden eureka moments

- ...joining, following, emerging and transforming-*with* over founding, visioning, authoring

- ...vague feeling, and sensing of what is odd and different of knowing what is clear and distinct

- ...creativity as a worldly process and not a human mental capacity

- ...experimental doing over removed ideation

- ...blocking the known and moving sideways

- ...that innovation does not set out to "solve" anything

- ...the non-linear

- ...the work of avoiding reducing things to essences, magic bullets, or origins

- ...multiplicity and variation, and integrate this into everything

- ...*processes* — this means developing and following procedures

- ...collaboration and collaborations over the illusion of individuality — all great acts of innovation and creativity happened collectively — with others (and not just human others)

- ...joy, surprise, curiosity

- ...schock, disgust, horror

- ...humility and wonder

155

Become:

- ...alien and playful
- ...sensitive to the liberating force of life, chaos, difference and creativity over the forces of law, order, repetition, and sameness
- ...an experiment: live life as an open experimental project
- ...a transdisciplinary networker, amateur, and generalist
- ...willing to trust the process
- ...comfortable with being confused, and that we will fail, and that there will be no guarantee in what we do
- ...OK with the fact that creativity will involve radical forms of rupture and betrayal of the given
- ...a great collaborator

Understand that:

- ... you will change
- ...creation as iterative (but not linear)
- ...assemblages matter
- ...everything is "networked" and relational (without a single author, or any author)
- That the "outcome" cannot be known in advance (& is not the final "purpose")
- That the origin of anything need not have any purpose, nor does it directly relate to its current use
- That the most interesting "traits" are nonadaptive (exaptive) –they are world opening (for a world that does not yet exist)
- Making/Thinking is a conjoined practice (not thinking then making). Ideas come later.
- Treat things as being active and having agency.
- Things shape us. Tools make us. Understand how this works.
- Innovation is messy, challenges our belief in solving

problems head on, and requires a lot of seemingly "useless" experimentation

- It is going to be messy (figuratively and literally). You need dedicated spaces

- It is going to take time – which will be hard to fit into a workshop, the regular work day, or a predefined sprint. New models need to be developed

- It is not based primarily in ideas (or in the mind).

- Things play a significant active role.

- Experiments invent their own criteria, questions/problems, fields, frameworks, and worlds.

- It is emergent--it involves following: wayfinding in waymaking.

- Causality isn't linear – it is crazy

- Creativity is not a willy-nilly free-for-all — there are processes

- ...creativity is creativity leadership. We are learning and teaching how to be comfortable leading oneself and others into discomfort and open-endedness. Play. Comfort. Seeing ethos and space.

Do:

- Cross thresholds from difference-in-degree to difference-in-kind

- Utilize the non-intended capacities of things and betray their original purpose

- Co-evolve with an environment

- Make a space that protects novelty (the lab) – keeps it away from "survival of the fittest" experiments/situations – and keep it away from having to be "something" as long as possible (needs to iteratively betray multiple "identities")

- Develop pirate projects-- probes into the unknown – open ended – perturbing a field – activating emergent unknowable (in advance) potentials – and then transforming with them...

- Use things as probes and not products

- Develop ways to understand and move between differing frameworks, cosmologies & paradigms (learn, collect, develop the knowledge of alternative frameworks)

- Train oneself to limit moral or factual judgements (follow practices, and ideas with an open mind). Stop the habit of being a "devil's advocate"

- Shift your focus from thinking about what something "is" to only considering: "What can it do?" This is a key disposition to acquire to have a truly experimental approach. Once you get good at asking "what can it do?" now ask: "and what else can it do?" Don't stop at one or two options, figure out 10 or more (this is where it gets interesting)

- Treat innovation/creativity as a process not a product.

- Worldmaking before problem tackling. Problem producing not problem solving. Problem producing before solution producing.

- Engage reality as a dynamic system and not composed of discrete things.

- It is a collective process (need to work & network with others--things, ideas, cultures, creatures, humans).

- Test, experiment, observe, multiply

- Work at a systems scale

- We need to move away from thinking of creativity as a thing – especially a mysterious internal property to be "unlocked". (The genius model).

- Invent rules and follow them (it won't be pregiven)

- ...we need to overcome our sense of self. Especially that we feel inadequate. "I'm not creative." "Why bother – every form of this has already been invented, nothing new can be done." This feeling will be the beginning of any creative endeavor. Ignore it. Push on. This feeling will always be there. Remember it is not about us.

be
like
a
crow

GLOSSARY

Affordance
> A term from ecological psychology, used to understand things by what they "afford" a user in contrast to understanding a thing based upon its explicit purpose. Example: A glass bottle's purpose is holding liquids, but one can discover that it affords one many ways to make sounds from tapping to blowing across the mouth. By privileging things affordances we open ourselves to a vast space of unintended possibilities which are critical to innovation. Much non-human innovation emerges via unintended affordances (See: Exaptation).
>
> What is critical is thinking about things not as what a thing "is" but what it can do. This is situational, relational and emergent. Because of this relation and emergent logic there is no end to the number of affordances.
>
> See: Gibson, and Deleuze in bibliography.

Agency
> The power of anything to affect and be affected by anything else.

Ambiguity
> We are taught to believe that we can have clear and distinct ideas because reality follows a plan which must be clear and distinct. But most of life is profoundly vague, dynamic, slippery, chaotic, uncertain and blurred.
>
> Novelty in its process of emergence is inherently vague and ambiguous. It cannot have any other state without being destroyed.
>
> We need to not only welcome ambiguity but develop techniques to actively work within this condition. This indeterminate logic means that

ideas are not the be all and end all of
innovation. In fact ideas play a small role in
the early stages of innovation -- they act as
hunches -- provocations to experiments.
Doing, making, following, co-evolving are all
more critical in the early phases of innovation.
Our cultural bias towards ideas is a huge
handicap to innovation.

See: Hunches, Vagueness, Emergence.

Autopoiesis:

Some things have the ability to make
themselves. Much of our classical
understanding falls apart because of a lack
of understanding that not all things need a
creator, plan or source. Autopoietic systems
can generate order and even life from
non-order.

Self-organizing systems under the right
conditions will spontaneously generate order.
Crowds will suddenly act in a unified manner,
plants will grow in specific forms and inanimate
materials will spontaneously take on certain
forms all without any hidden regulating or
organizing substrate (genes, rules, plans etc.).
The emergence of novel worlds requires
working within the logic of self-organizing
systems.

Becoming

Non-developmental change. Change in kind
where the "change" has no subject distinct from
itself. A "block" of becoming. Opposite of
development.

Blocking

Technique to stop repeating what is known.
Creativity = not repeating what has already
been done. Creativity is often mistakenly
defined as "complete freedom" or "no rules"

but that is not the case. Innovation requires strong rules to refuse existing rules, patterns, tools, habits and worldviews.

Blocking is a refusal and the beginning of a process of experimentation: "if we no longer can do this, what can we now do?"

Blocking, while it might sound simple or crude, is a sophisticated form of "enabling constraint". It enables a difference to be nurtured by constraining the norm, but only if the choice of what to block is well chosen.

Blocking is a nuanced activity that first requires knowing the existing rules patterns techniques etc. so that they can be effectively blocked. The key to blocking is to disclose an existing paradigm or world, and this is itself a phase (Disclose) of innovation.

See: Disclose, World, Rules, Enabling Constraint.

Betrayal

Paradigmatic innovation requires betrayal. Paradigmatic change is not an improvement of an existing world, but a total rupture. You will need to leave a world behind. This is a very difficult thing to do. You will feel deeply torn, uncertain and out of your depth. You will be judged as crazy, mistaken, dumb... On top of this you will have no guarantee that you are onto anything worthwhile. This state of being is not the same as being comfortable with failure. It is a deeply unsettling uncertainty that does not go away.

Care

Care for the event, care for the experiment.

See: Sympathy.

Chance:

Chance is everywhere, and critical to everything -- all innovations surf chance -- innovators harness it. It is a wonderful method to remove classical forms of authorship. It has been well developed by artists and designers as part of algorithmic techniques.

See: John Cage, Olipo in bibliography.

Change

Change comes in two forms: change in degree and change in kind.

Creativity — Psychological

Confusion, assumes creativity is a thing that can be located in the brain of humans. Standard model.

Creativity

A process to develop novelty. Two forms: degree kind. Question of difference. Pure difference, differing.

'Creativity' is the universal of universals characterizing ultimate matter of fact. It is that ultimate principle by which the many, which are the universe disjunctively, become the one actual occasion, which is the universe conjunctively. It lies in the nature of things that the many enter into complex unity."
A. N. Whitehead

Crisis Thinking

A mindset that prioritizes urgency over a considered response: "Things are so bad that if we do not act now it will be a total disaster!" or "We need to act now, doing something is better than nothing!" This leads to a deepening of the problem rather than any solution. It is common in environmental issues such as Global Warming. Crisis thinking leads to dangerous feedback loops that escalate the problem: "See, we did not act soon enough or fully, and now the problem is so much bigger -- now we really need to act as big and quickly as possible!"

See: Solution Thinking and Thing Thinking for related conceptual framework errors.

Co-Evolution

This gets to the chicken vs egg paradox (N+C Paradigm). We can leave behind such logics if we carefully understand how complex systems participate in co-making. The thing and its environment co-make each other.

A process where you and the "thing" you are making shape and transform each other. Both the "product" and the community of users come into being via this process. The key insight is, you are not making a product after which you will discover a community of "users."

The process of design co-evolves the users and the product in an iterative loop of co-development and co-specification. This process stands in deliberate contrast to ideas of "customer discovery" and "customer validation" or the prototyping process in design thinking.

See: Emergence.

Collaborator

Specific people + things + processes + paradigms + environments that you need to work with on any phase of a project. Critical is to realize that the agent of innovation is the collaboration (the whole).

Note: They do not stay with you for the entirety of a project, this changes with phases.

Confirmation Bias

It means that we always look for the evidence to support our views. On a deeper level everything we see, say and do in our everyday mode of attention confirms our views.

While this issue is well recognized, the real question is much deeper. We do not all live in the same neutral reality which we just see differently based upon our biases (or cultures or world views etc.).

This model of diving reality into (1) the really real and (2) interpretations is itself flawed.

See: World, Reality Divided, Data Blind.

Context

Being sensitive to context is not the same as assuming that context is a case of following a set or contextual rules (general to particular). Nothing is reducible to history or context. Becoming is irreducible to history/context -- these are necessary but only that. what they can do/become is an open question.

See: Emergence.

Data Blind

Your observations undermine the possibility of your worldview, but you cannot see it because your worldview is so strong.

Deficit Model

The belief that people only lack info and if they had it they would act.

Design

The process of making. Both human and non-human. Both material and immaterial. At many scales.

Over the last century the term "design" has referred to the making of things, and the term "designers" has referred to those who make these things. (Usually these are useful things as opposed "non-useful" things which have been historically categorized as "art".)

Critical here is that design as a term and as a field is much broader than the making of concrete objects. Design is a process to shape movements, transform systems, develop concepts and make things. This needs to be taken further, design as a process is not just reducible to human practices. Design is the process of making -- whether human or not. This is important for many reasons, not the least of which is that human making is always embedded in larger and smaller non-human processes. It behooves the human designer to understand that they are part of multiple other non-human processes.

Design Thinking

A user-centered design strategy that is a form of developmental design. Focus is on empathizing with users and asking about their problems and needs. Steps: Empathize, Ideate, Prototype, Make.

A popularized model of various engaged and user-centered models of design, all of which have real advantages over historical models of Direct Design. While empathizing is important, Design Thinking is not an effective method to develop disruptive or paradigmatic innovations. Additionally, by being an "ideate first" process it has all of the pitfalls of direct design in terms of developing any form of real novelty.

See: Making.

Development

A step by step process of improvement.
A change in degree, not kind. Opposite of
becoming.

Developmental Design

Forms of design that are best suited to
development vs qualitative change. User
Centered Design and its variants (such as
Design Thinking) are good examples.

Deviate

Phase of the Innovation Design process.

Difference

Change. Normal assumption is that difference
comes after identity: difference is a change.
This is only a difference in degree. Pure difference is a difference that precedes identity:
no copy model or origin. Two types:
1. difference in degree
2. difference in kind

Difference in Degree

Difference in kind when pushed across a
threshold.

Difference in Kind

Small changes or iterations.

Direct Design

Best understood as the "fallacy of direct
design". Historical model of idea driven linear
design (illusion). Ideate--Model--Make.

Innovation: "as in actual life, we make detours,
we go by side-roads. We see the straight
highway before us, but of course we cannot
use it..." Wittgenstein.

See: Developmental Design, Responsive Design.

Disclose
> Phase of the Innovation Design process.

Dynamic
> Nothing is static, everything is process -- fields and processes. Stability is the temporary dynamic state of one phase of a system. Feedback loops will tip the system into another state. The set of these linked states or phases produce a type of meta-stable condition. Movement is form coming into being (without necessarily following a plan).

Emerge
> Phase of the Innovation Design process.

Emergence
> Process of Innovation comes about not via some mysterious or mystical internal process but via the process of emergence. Emergence is the technical term for a process of coming into being that exceeds and supersedes its inputs. Smaller events/components come in unpredictable manners that are irreducible to the logic of the component parts. It is a form of non-linear and non-incremental change (change in degree).
>
> Emergence: This process is the key to all forms of creativity that avoid the N+C Paradigm. It is how something seems to emerge from "nothing". It is the process by which the new emerges from the old. In the most simple terms: it's the process by which things emerge that are:
> 1. Greater than the sum of their parts.
> 2. Irreducible to their parts. And...
> 3. make their own parts.
>
> There are many examples of emergence all around us -- that we are conscious beings -- is a classical example of emergence. Consciousness

is something that requires having a brain, but is irreducible to the brain, and it changes the brain. Why does this matter for creativity? We so often understand making as a process of addition. We add parts together and get a whole (Think of how we assembled things with Lego as a child). Here the parts make the whole and the whole can be taken back apart and each part can be analyzed to understand the whole. This is a reductive model of making. We can reduce the final product to the parts and the process. Cars can be built this way. But the genuinely new does not come about in this manner.

Empathy

In distinction to Sympathy. Component of sympathy. More than psychological.

Engage

Phase of Innovation Design

Enaction

Way to understand a being's relation to their environment and how they co-create and co-enable each other. Developed from Cognitive Psychology. Understands humans (or any other being) to be embodied, embedded, extended, enactive and affective. Critical alternative to the classical view of human-world relation.

Enabling Constraint

A term Erin Manning & Brian Massumi coined for rules that limit actions to enable novelty.

See: Blockage & Rules.

Escalation

Much of our solution oriented thinking that ignores the systemic nature of reality tends to escalate the very issues it is trying to address.

E.g. addressing hunger by sending surplus grain to Africa has led to the collapse of farming as prices are held artificially below what is sustainable for an african farmer. This is usually the outcome of taking problems to be objective.

Event

Always excessive. There is always more than. Seed of newness.

See: Exaptive

Equity Centered Design

Inclusive form of community design

Exaptation

This is the evolutionary process of utilizing the unintended consequences (affordances) of a physical feature to novel ends. Most, if not all, critical features of organisms evolved in this manner: wings, eyes, bones etc.

Darwin originally called these phenomenon "preadaptation," but this suggests that the creature was somehow preparing for this novel features emergence (that it could know in advance about flight). Recently, Stephen Jay Gould and Elizabeth Verba proposed that this be called: exaptation, because it is outside (the ex part of the term) adaptation. Which is a beautiful way of describing creativity -- it is a process of novelty that is outside of fitting into any existing purpose.

See: Gould in bibliography.

Excess

Creativity relies on the excess of each and every moment, thing, process and event.

Experiment

How do we do things experimentally? Stop asking "what is it?"

In terms of creativity it does not matter "what it is." What matters for an experimental approach is: What can it do? This is curiosity in a nutshell -- to keep asking of things and events, what else can it do? And what else can you do? This can only happen by doing -- not just thinking. Things will surprise you when you push them beyond their supposed purpose. (Your chair is a tool for scraping and these glorious scraping sounds are the beginning of a new musical genre...).

Things will rupture your comfortable assumptions about what they "are" (they are, in fact, doing it all the time -- we just choose to ignore them). Asking "what is it?" sends you back into the past and the known (the dictionary of good and proper definitions). "What can it do?" ask you to put things into new contexts, environments and connections -- into creative play -- now you are in the middle of a relational and experimentally open question.

Explaining Away

When novelty -- a difference -- first emerges it is quite fragile and prone to be mis-recognized as what already exists. It is very hard to see difference as a difference.

Two dangerous but very common habits that erase difference is [1] our tendency to Universalize, or [2] reduce things to a form of Utility.

See: Universalizing, Utility-as-the-answer.

Idea

Never at the origin of newness and radical creativity. The cause of the new is never an idea. the idea/conceptualization of the new comes later — often much later. It is both a serious conceptual error to posit an idea at the beginning of an innovation and a methodological error in developing an innovation design process.

See: Intention, Direct Design, Design Thinking, Emergence, Enaction.

Immersion

Synonym for the Engagement Phase of the Innovation Design process.

See: Engagement.

Indirect / Non-linear

Disruptive innovation. Non-prediction. Innovation: "as in actual life, we make detours, we go by side-roads. We see the straight highway before us, but of course we cannot use it..." Wittgenstein.

Innovation

Differences producing difference via threshold searching and crossing.

Innovation Design (Approach)

Design process for activating creative and innovative potentials in any context. Consists of four phases: Engage, Disclose, Deviate, and Emerge.

See: Design, Engage, Disclose, Deviate, Emerge, and Immersion.

Intention

Creativity surfs the productive gap between intention, and use, engagement, or actuality.

Making
> Making as thinking

Matter of Concern
> More general and abstract way to articulate an initial "problem". key to avoiding "solution thinking."

Map
> Not a representation of the terrain but a tool to engage with the terrain.

Mediator
> Transducer.

Newness Paradox
> See: Innovation Paradox.

Open
> Seems like such a simple term. Open means that every final closure or summary is simply another "thing" beside everything else in the system. Open relates to all of these terms. Open does not mean "anything goes", but it is quite a wild and disturbing term. When you are finished the winds come in from the open to expose you to what happens next -- for which we can never be ready... Perhaps the only source of great joy or humor.

Paradigm
> Mindset -- goals, rules, structures and parameters arise.

> See: World.

Paradigm shift
> Fundamental change in kind

Play
> Putter, tinker.

Problem

Easily misunderstood as "something to solve or overcome". Well stated problems already include all possible answers. A further misunderstanding is that innovation is focused on how one solves problems. This is wrong. Innovation is at its most creative when it invents new problems.

Problem-Solution Coupling

Interdependence between a problem and its solutions.

Probe

Not customer validation. Rather, co-evolve moment.

See: Co-evolve.

Process

Reality is composed of processes. Nothing is simply a discrete object. Everything comes into being via a process, stays in existence via another process, and transforms out of being via yet other processes. To innovate is to see, think, and live processes.

Proposition

A proposition is the articulating of a tendency sensed in an experiment (event).

Relations/relationality

The fixed state of all things. Things are always connected and one could further state that [1] the connection (relation) is a thing in itself, and that [2] "things" are their connections.

See: Emergence.

Realism

A call to be "realistic" -- a claim that change is necessary but real change is "unrealistic" -- very common call around issues of global warming or climate change.

Romantic Creation

That creativity is the absence of conditions and rules. Determinism vs negation. Idea vs spontaneity. False choice.

Solution

Solutions are "answers" to a problem. Problems are really ways of posing a question. Any question determines a possible field of answers. Thus solutions never come alone and are ultimately only as good as the question being asked (along with its underlying assumptions).

As designers/makers we often fall in love with our solutions (answers). This is a mistake (from the perspective of creativity). We need to fall in love with the possibility of becoming the creators of problems worth having.
See: Problem, Problems Worth Having.

Solution Thinking

taking a problem and all of its implicit assumptions for granted and only focusing on solving the problem as it is given. Leads to very limited forms of innovation and most often a repetition of the underlying issue.

Systems

Set of elements or parts coherently organized and interconnected.

Stakeholder

People you cannot ignore. Those who are part of the ecosystem of your matter of concern. (This is not an ideal term.)

Success Bias

This is also related to what is called in systems thinking: success to the successful. It is really easy to fall into the trap of rewarding what has succeeded so far -- painters know about painting and so they reward what they know -- it goes for race, forms of transportation, and so on.

Sympathy

"What things feel when they shape each other."

See: Things, Bibliography: Sypbrok.

Tendencies

During experiments the field often self organizes around certain spontaneously emerging tendencies. These are cues towards possible novel emergences.
See: Experimentation, Following, Event.

Thing

An active x. Things are not passive nor are they our intentions.

Thing Thinking

A belief that the world is composed of discrete things and not systems. The desire to see everything as a thing (e.g. creativity). Corrective: systems thinking, dynamic systems theory (DST).

See: Emergence, Systems, Process, Feedback and Feedforward.

Transformation

A worldview without creativity. Anthropological turn.

Tuning

Creativity requires attunement. We do not begin as "authors" or "makers" -- we begin by tuning ourselves to the rhythms of a novel event. One needs to develop a very serious practice of creating a mode of attunement.

Universalizing

A problematic process for ignoring or denying differences that matter. "We are all the same..." Additionally a problematic answer to questions: we should all aspire to the same solution--a classical model of this is all of the Western answers to social questions: Development, Capitalism, Liberal Democracy -- as if this was the sum total of all humanity's possibilities.

Unintended Consequences

Or consequences. There are only consequences (See: Intention). Creativity utilizes the unintended. All newness is part or wholly unintended. In this manner we cannot write-off unintended consequences as negative, for they are wholly productive and edging into the new.

Utility-as-answer

Habit of explaining any situation or object via "utility". This is a common form of world-blindness. Universal explanations.... to make useful or to fit into the past. The trivial and the useful are not distinct from the perspective of making.

World

All thoughts, ideas, concepts and practices necessarily depend upon a space of implicit "pre-understanding." This pre-understanding hangs together in a holistic manner. Implicit set of embodied practices, environments, ecologies, tools and mentalities (mindset) that ground and support a way of seeing, understanding and engaging with reality.

Can be very general (e.g. the "western" worldview) or can be more specific (e.g. Plus the habits, and the physical systems that support and reinforce this.)

World Making

Experimental process of making a world. Key process for innovation. (See: World). An event self coordinating and coming to value. Never done. Never plug and play -- you cannot "switch" worlds. Speculative -- for a people still to come (Deleuze).

Worlding

Synonym for worldmaking

World Blind

Not able to see that things are always of a world. Being world blind is most often a condition of innovation: in making something radically new it is very difficult to see that it is the harbinger of a totally new world (paradigm).

Being world blind is only a problem if one cannot transition out of it to sensing the novel world / paradigm. Most often innovators are too close to their innovation to sense the world that they are ushering into being.

Note: Opposite: Data blind: Your observations

undermine the possibility of your worldview, but you cannot see it because your worldview is so strong.

X   The unknowable that fringes all action with radical possibility.

put
the
ladder
down

ABOUT US

Jason Frasca – **Founding Partner**

Jason is a native New Yorker — born and raised in the New York City metro, worked in and around every borough, and pretty much seen everything the city does from the back of his motorbike.

Really from birth, Jason has been an urban innovator, sleuth of futures bubbling up in the sidewalk cracks, and anthropologist of everyday lives.

Since childhood Jason has been hacking systems and imaginatively speculating on alternative futures — he likes to say that he was the family innovation consultant by the time he got to preschool. These formative experiences led him to become an entrepreneurial business executive, marketing, and sales professional managing Fortune 500 and nationally recognized clients in many diverse sectors of the economy from direct marketing, non-profit, entrepreneurship, startups, private investigations, insurance, and international law. In each of these sectors, he brought systemic and transformative innovation that combined astute trend analysis and the right level of disruptive envisioning to push companies into blue ocean spaces.

Because of his unique approach and diverse experience midway through all of this Jason was recruited to higher ed to become part of the core faculty to invent a new entrepreneurship and innovation program.

He envisioned and brought the first maker space to a school of business and began a renaissance in how entrepreneurship, innovation, and design are taught in business schools.

From being a pioneer to now part of developing a movement to transform innovation education in general Jason has put people, the planet, and meaningful innovation at the heart of his approach to teaching. On almost any given day Jason can be found collaborating with colleagues deconstructing complex problems and providing a systems design approach to the collective invention of new possibilities. In his role as an academic Jason has worked on program-level curriculum development, invented new ways to teach students via intensives, international retreats, immersive travel programs, long-term mentorship, and transformed the infrastructure of the school.

From those rough and tumble days in New York City to the innovation consultant of today Jason has dedicated his career to designing radically innovative technology solutions and processes for companies, communities, and ecosystems with a visionary and pragmatic mindset that has yielded massive results with limited resources.

Iain Kerr – **Founding Partner**
Iain is a west coast kid who grew up in a very different Vancouver in an era of visionaries and dreamers. He remembers the sailing of Greenpeace boats and summers swimming in the harbor. He spent years climbing mountains and this deep immersion in the wilderness led him to research philosophy, ecology, complexity science, and evolutionary theory and convince him of the radical power of being generalist for innovation and creativity.

Those formative years led Iain to become a designer working at the intersection of creativity, ecology, and emergent systems — always with the goal: to make novel worlds possible. His unique approach evolves from over twenty plus years of experimenting across and beyond the zones of Architecture, Design, Ecology, Art, Creativity Studies, Ethnobotany, Food Studies, Systems Thinking, Social Entrepreneurship, Commons Studies and Philosophy. His focus when working as an innovation consultant is on designing novel collective processes to transform seemingly intractable problems into, as he put it "problems worth having for worlds worth making".

Like Jason, Iain was brought into start a new entrepreneurship program at Montclair State University, where together they are Co-Director's of the MIX Lab (Making and Innovating for X). The MIX Lab's mission is to foster innovation at all scales.

In addition to co-directing the MIX Lab, Iain is a co-founder of the boundary-blurring design consultancy SPURSE and the Emergent Futures Lab.

SPURSE has been at the forefront of ecological research, experimental design, and innovation leadership for the last 15 years. While developing ground-breaking ways to probe, catalyze, disrupt and re-imagine systems both large and small, they have collaborated with communities, organizations, and individuals from the high arctic to inner cities neighborhoods in Bolivia. Their award-winning projects reveal an astonishing range of creative solutions to effecting real change: from restaurants, wetlands, wayfinding apps, urban renewal programs, microbiology laboratories, cookbooks, buildings, everyday tools and more.

In 2018 Iain and Jason Frasca founded Emergent Futures Lab as a platform for the rethinking of creativity, invention, and change — what they are, how they are realized, and how they can be taught. The Emergent Futures Lab has developed a number of new tools including the Innovation Design Approach.

Iain regularly works as a consultant, lecturer and workshop leader on creativity, innovation, and design (MIT, Harvard University, Columbia University, Parsons, Yale, CCA, and RISD). His most recent research is on developing new models of Innovation that are collective, enactive, materially engaged forms of novel worldmaking: Innovation Design. His and SPURSE's work has been discussed in books and journals from the NYTimes, ID, and Surface to The International Encyclopedia of Human Geography.

Now as Iain looks back from his early days hanging off a cliffs ledge to exploring the coasts of British Columbia he finds the similar adventure and joy in carrying out the work of Emergent Futures Lab internationally.

Emergent Futures Lab
A strategic innovation consulting firm.

Some refer to us as "Blue Sky" consultants. That stuffs us into a box. We don't like boxes. We prefer to tear the box up and create entirely new spaces of possibility. Because our award winning innovation program is about more than just creating product differentiation and inventing new markets.

We help make all types of innovation happen.
From co-evolving new paradigms to developing transformative innovation cultures. We are passionate about evolving existing products and services in unintended novel ways, and how we can use radical innovation to meet our 21st century challenges from social to the climate crisis.

The fact is, we get fired up about one thing:
How to Innovate

Sure, we spend our free time deconstructing innovations to understand where and why products, services and markets evolve and flourish while others wither into irrelevance. But what gets us up every morning is working with people, communities, and companies to innovate meaningful possibilities.

Let's connect and innovate something beautiful together,

Iain Kerr: iain@emergentfutureslab.com
Jason Frasca: jason@emergentfutureslab.com

Want to learn more? Visit our website:
emergentfutureslab.com

Acknowledgments
This book has been many years in the making.

Over the last two decades the research and the development of the big ideas/practices behind this project were carried out in the field by members of the design collective SPURSE.
From there we have developed, tested and refined various models and formats — going through countless versions for different projects and classes. Everyone we worked with in this process, especially students and community members, has had a critical and creative role in shaping this for the better.

Since 2017 we have been collaborating with the entre-preneurship team at the Karl-Franzens University of Graz, Austria. Our colleagues there have had a formative hand in making this what it is.

At our academic home base: the MIX Lab @ Montclair State University, the whole team has played many important roles. We thank each and everyone of you — you have shaped this, and us, for the better.
Thank you.

wonder
discordant
adventure
unknowable
next